CONQUERING YOUR AGORAPHOBIA

Mona Woodford MBE

JAVELIN BOOKS
POOLE · NEW YORK · SYDNEY

First published in the UK 1987 by Javelin Books,
Link House, West Street, Poole, Dorset BH15 1LL

Distributed in the United States by
Sterling Publishing Co., Inc.,
2 Park Avenue, New York, NY 10016

Distributed in Australia by
Capricorn Link (Australia) Pty Ltd,
PO Box 665, Lane Cove, NSW 2066

British Library Cataloguing in Publication Data

Woodford, Mona
  Conquering your agoraphobia.
  1. Agoraphobia — Treatment
  I. Title
  616.85'225   RC552.A44

ISBN 0 7137 1788 2

Typeset by Word Perfect 99 Ltd, Bournemouth, Dorset.

Printed and bound in Great Britain by
Cox & Wyman Ltd, Reading

CONTENTS

AUTHOR'S NOTE

This book is written in a spirit of hope and optimism and is based on my personal experience of agoraphobia and 21 years' involvement with a national organisation, formed to help people with anxiety and phobias (agoraphobia in particular).

The aim is to give understanding through explanation, encouragement through hope and a more optimistic outlook through the experiences of others who are now fully recovered.

HE WHO DELIBERATES FULLY BEFORE TAKING A STEP WILL SPEND HIS ENTIRE LIFE ON ONE LEG

(Chinese proverb)

ACKNOWLEDGEMENTS

To Eric, always.

To Brenda Griffiths, my sincerest thanks for her help and support throughout, especially for the mammoth task of typing the manuscript.

To the many agoraphobes who allowed their stories or case histories, albeit anonymously, to be quoted in our pages, my thanks.

Mona Woodford
1986

FOREWORD

So you think you are agoraphobic? Let us ponder on the meaning of the word 'agoraphobia'. It is derived from two Greek words: *phobos* meaning 'fear' and *agora* meaning 'a place of assembly or market-place'. The sufferers from this fear describe it in different ways, according to the way in which it affects them. Some will say that it is a fear of meeting people or crowds, others a fear of empty spaces, still others a fear of leaving a place of safety. People vary enormously in the degree of the panic attacks which are the cause of the fear, but the basis lies in anxiety. This is a condition which we shall examine very thoroughly throughout these pages.

Reading this book should put to rest some of the secret fears which cause many people to stay in the 'rut' to which they have become accustomed. However, only when you can convince yourself that the 'panics' are only *feelings* will you regain your lost confidence and start living again as you used to before . . . after all, you were not born this way.

Remember too, that you are *not* a coward. An agoraphobe can be classed as one of the most courageous people around, especially whilst striving to live a 'normal' life, even though struggling to overcome inner anxieties.

Agoraphobia is not a unique state nowadays and you certainly are not alone with your suffering; many thousands in all walks of life are coping and eventually recovering, albeit with patience and perseverance on their part.

CONQUERING YOUR AGORAPHOBIA

1 · WHAT IS AGORAPHOBIA?

Although the definition of agoraphobia is 'a morbid fear of public places', not just open spaces as is commonly thought, the panic sensations can come over people in enclosed spaces and, in many cases, even when they are alone in their own homes. It will be a relief to know, as you read this, that so many others understand exactly how you feel.

The most difficult part of the condition is the almost continual state of anxiety and apprehension you experience. After all, it is not really a particular *situation* that you are afraid of but the awful feelings you have when in that situation. Most agoraphobes suffer from claustrophobia as well and it is often difficult to sort out where agoraphobia stops and claustrophobia begins. One definition of agoraphobia is 'fear of a situation from which you feel there is no immediate escape.'

Symptoms (which vary greatly from person to person) can include a terrifying feeling of unreality — as if walking in a nightmare — dizziness, palpitations, shortness of breath, dry mouth, clammy hands, a 'jelly-legs' sensation of leaning to one side when walking, buzzing in the head, tension cramps anywhere in the body, difficulty in swallowing and even a climax such as a stroke, heart attack or 'brainstorm', or fainting through overbreathing. All these conditions are discussed later in the book.

Often people will admit, when looking back, that the acute attack of panic first occurred after a period of stress, illness, accident or bereavement. Agoraphobia often starts as a result of delayed shock. The trouble is that you begin to make a habit of panic so that, every time you travel on a bus, reach a certain dreaded 'spot', or find yourself in a queue in the supermarket, the feeling threatens to overwhelm you and it is this that is so frightening. So many people at this stage begin to avoid their panic situations, the distance which they will go from home becomes shorter and shorter, until at last their fears prevent them even going outside their own front door. This habit of fear must be broken somehow and knowing that others have overcome it and now lead normal lives should encourage you to take comfort. At least you will realise that you are no longer struggling alone and are certainly not unique in your condition. A deeper understanding of the condition and how to go about overcoming it yourself all play a part in helping towards recovery.

It has been estimated that about 10 persons in every 1,000 worldwide suffer from agoraphobia to a lesser or greater degree, which makes about 500,000 sufferers in the UK; 70% of all sufferers are women. These figures should give you a feeling of overwhelming relief in the realisation that so many others experience the same unpleasant symptoms.

Although many are curing themselves, some perhaps taking drugs to ease the tension, many others have been battling along alone, keeping their secret from family and friends (and sometimes even their doctors), and wondering what on earth was the matter with them, fearing that perhaps they were going mad or were suffering from some horrible brain disease!

HOW DOES AGORAPHOBIA START?

Agoraphobia usually follows on from a series of instances, or an isolated instance, of tremendous anxiety or shock. It may be that the victim has endured some terrible pressing problem from which there appeared to be no escape.

The prime agony of agoraphobia is a panic attack. You, as a victim, know exactly what a 'panic attack' is by its side effects. When you tell your doctor or a psychiatrist that you have panic attacks he probably will not know what you are talking about. He may not understand that agoraphobia is not so much a fear of open spaces but a fear of experiencing, once again, a 'panic'. In most cases, it is the first single, mysterious, unaccountable terrible fear which establishes the ensuing pattern, an experience so bad that the sufferer will do anything to avoid its recurrence.

Typical agoraphobic personalities are people with finely-etched nerves, not necessarily nervous but nervy. They are usually very fast in speech, thought and action or reaction. They may be more intelligent than average, go-getters and extrovert. They love life and ignore pressures: until they are struck down with that primary attack of panic, caused by a sudden thrust of adrenalin into the bloodstream, everything has been fairly normal in all respects. Some have had a full social life prior to this attack. Some have been big worriers. They are all, or mostly, people who have talent, especially artistically.

The main trouble with agoraphobia victims is that they feel they have been completely and utterly divested of their confidence. It is not surprising that the impact of the original trauma plus the accompanying physical manifestations are sufficient to immobilise the sufferer. The dread of a recurrence virtually writes off the possibility of a normal existence. Victims sometimes cannot get as far as their doctor's surgery. They cannot shop, make social visits, see films or plays, have a meal in a restaurant, attend their children's school functions, or do anything which was formerly normal, everyday activity. If they were going out to work, they can no longer earn a living. If they are running a home they cannot possibly cope as they did before the illness struck them down. They cannot even get treatment for everyday ills, such as headaches and toothaches, because visiting doctors and dentists is impossible unless someone accompanies them. The trials and tribulations of the sufferers are manifold and alarming. The additional pressures and stresses of trying to live normal lives serve only to exacerbate the overall intolerable situation.

Why is this malady on the increase? Nobody seems interested in knowing. Current victims are stigmatised as nut-cases, mentally retarded, cowards, misfits, malingerers, neurotics or weirdies.

CASE HISTORIES

The following extracts are taken from letters sent to 'Open Door', the U.K. association which deals with agoraphobia.

Jack tells us: I used to think that a physical disability would be preferable to agoraphobia because at least people could be easily told what was wrong. Last year I watched my father in the last hours of his fight against lung cancer . . . Next time I feel weak and breathless I shall think 'Thank God it is only temporary'. I used to think for a man to have agoraphobia was much worse than for a woman, because I had to be the breadwinner and in my case I was expected to be strong. A female friend shocked me by saying how much worse it was for a woman and went on to describe all the things she had to do every day, all the fears she had to overcome and convinced me I was the lucky one! . . . On the morning of my departure for a recent holiday there appeared on my doormat a postcard from a friend wishing me luck. Who cares about agoraphobia with a friend like that? A little encouragement perhaps is the answer to anyone who nearly gives up.

Barbara tells us: I'm so excited to tell you that I have made much progress in the last few weeks — at one time I could only go out with my 17-year-old daughter who has been wonderfully patient and even then I had to stand by the shop door whilst she did the shopping. However, about three weeks ago, I felt the urge to *try* and, after going into the shops with her standing by, I was eventually able to do most things alone and even venture into one or two shops myself when I felt brave enough. One day I even went through the town alone and, as ours is a seaside resort and packed with holidaymakers, that was a major achievement . . . but I still could not face the supermarket as it was equipped with one-way turnstiles. However, last weekend, my daughter persuaded me to have a go and I managed really well but today I went alone and I felt tremendous! Although I am prepared for setbacks I consider myself well on the way to recovery. My advice to fellow sufferers is to wait until they feel that *urge* and then work with it like mad. The feeling of being able to go out is wonderful. My step is lighter, my smile more ready and the sense of achievement beyond description.

These two case histories are typical examples of how much better you can become after changing your attitude towards a problem. Can you remember your Latin from schooldays? Were you taught *festina lente* (make haste slowly)? It works wonders in the majority of difficult situations.

SOME FACTS AND FIGURES ABOUT AGORAPHOBICS

A survey of 1,200 agoraphobics by Professor Isaac Marks in the UK in 1970 yielded the following information.

1. *Age* The average age of female sufferers is 31 or 32 years — (youngest 15 years and oldest 83 years). Among my favourite comments given to women by doctors is 'It's your age'. Teenagers are invariably told 'You'll grow out of it,' and sexual frustration is often blamed in the case of women in their early 20s. The 'effort of running a home and caring for the family' seems to be responsible among married women in their late 20s and early 30s and, from 35 onwards, 'the change' and 'old age' become popular as explanations. The average age of males is around 35 years (but I don't think any of them have been told that their phobias are due to their age!).

2. *Marital status* About 25% of sufferers are single. Most of them are (with difficulty) managing to hold down jobs. I have known 5 doctors, 35 nurses, 40 school teachers, 11 professional musicians, both performers and teachers, several high-powered business women and a couple of journalists. (Shades of that 'above-average intelligence'.)

3. *Contacts* About 50% of sufferers do not want contact with other sufferers, a fact which surprises the other half, who do. The sort of people who wish to keep their agoraphobia secret include:
a) professional people who feel it might endanger their careers.

19

b) women whose husbands are well-known in the area where they live (eg. doctors' wives).

c) wives who are fighting their condition and managing to hide it from husbands and families.

d) those with unsympathetic spouses who won't understand or even try to! This also applies to families.

e) people who are frightened of 'catching' symptoms from contacts.

4. *Duration of agoraphobia* The average time was 10 years but this included many who had had their phobias from childhood. Furthermore, the average was pushed up by older people who had put up with the problem for 20 to 30 years without doing anything about it. Discounting these, the average was 2 to 3 years.

5. *Types of treatment undertaken* These included: drugs, psychoanalysis, narco-analysis, group therapy, hypnosis, auto-suggestion, behaviour therapy, and hospital in-patient or day-centre attendance.

6. *Success of treatment* 20% of those surveyed thought that the treatment undergone definitely helped; 10% thought it helped a little and 70% thought it did not help at all. The most successful treatment to date is self desensitisation, i.e. self-help possibly with a short-term programme of tranquillisers or anti-depressants from a doctor.

7. *Theories as to the trigger of the condition* Some sufferers had experienced a traumatic childhood but many people's symptoms seem to have developed soon after some serious illness, such as an operation, childbirth or an accident, a severe emotional shock or a long period of emotional tension such as difficult family situations without resolve.

CLAUSTROPHOBIA AND AGORAPHOBIA

Did you know that claustrophobia often went hand in hand with agoraphobia? Think of a person who panics in a crowded supermarket: it is not always fear of the crowds but a fear of the feeling of being hemmed in, which is just as real as being panicky when travelling on a subway or using an elevator, or indeed in any confined space.

Most of us admit to having very mild feelings of claustrophobia even when reading about or seeing people on T.V. who are down mines or under the sea in submarines. Probably more people suffer from these feelings in varying degrees than from any other phobia, indeed it is so common that it merits very little consideration in the main.

Naturally there is a small minority who react with very severe panics to some situations even to the extent that they cannot contemplate entering an elevator, travelling on a subway or entering any building where they are likely to encounter large numbers of people. These folk need help from their medical practitioner who may in turn pass them on to a psychologist to talk over their sensitisation to these situations.

To de-sensitise oneself it has to be realised that a good deal of willpower is needed to gradually enter the 'dreaded' place, at first making sure of an exit in case of dire need — and staying a little longer each time over a long period, until the choking, smothering feelings no longer distress and you are able to face the fear without panicking.

Many claustrophobics have a fear of various kinds of travel, either by plane, boat or even car, being convinced that without complete control of the vehicle themselves or at best one particular driver whom they trust, they are going to panic. This attitude restricts movement away from home in ever decreasing circles, thus bringing them back to an agoraphobic situation. Paradoxically some agoraphobes suffer the fears of claustrophobia when in their own home, alone.

One other point with regard to a 'hemmed in' feeling is that of being trapped in an unsatisfactory marital situation, where either partner becomes resentful and yet conscience stricken because they want the partnership to end.

Very often too, a woman may feel 'trapped' because she is the one expected to care for aged parents without help and the prospect fills her with dismay if it is long term.

The above situations can only be dealt with by complete family discussion to find a way in which the members of the family can be rallied round to provide breaks from the routine.

Michael tells us: I'm principally afraid of open spaces but also cannot travel by train. I have had two major breakdowns and think my experience may be of interest to other sufferers. The trouble began when I was studying at university at the age of 21. My first breakdown followed my anxieties about attending lectures. For about seven years I virtually gave up hope of finding a way through my fears. I always seemed to struggle the wrong way and although I held down a job for a while I ended up at home and just wanted to die. I had a second breakdown which was a traumatic experience but astonishingly new hope was born. I thought at last I could tackle my fears. I have not beaten them yet. The glimpse of hope I caught has been a flighty thing but buoys me up at present. What will the future bring? Others appear to be more confident than I but perhaps I can be optimistic. If I should lose my hope again perhaps it will not be forever.

Bernard says: After contacts with a number of people suffering from agoraphobia I have come to the conclusion they are not in fact suffering from fear of open spaces, it appears to me the condition could be more aptly descrined as phobophobia, which is fear of fear itself. People are not so much afraid of certain situations they may find themselves in as their own reactions to those situations. I believe to some extent my own experience confirms this view. After living alone for a number of years I found myself in severely depressive state. Confidence was almost non-existent and minor problems became major obstacles. Over sensitised I found myself thinking about everyday situations and how to react to them. The result was that I became afraid of my own reactions instead of 'feeling' my way through. However, last year I attacked the problem on two fronts by learning to swim and doing voluntary work for the Probation Service. Having always been afraid of water since a child the former took quite an effort but eventually I was successful. Overcoming a real fear I personally believe can help when it comes to irrational fears.

OTHER PHOBIAS

Although we are primarily dealing with agoraphobia and its associated social impairments in this book, it is worth mentioning for your interest that there are very many other phobias. Although these cause some distress to the sufferer, they rarely affect lifestyle as radically as does agoraphobia.

There are some 130 other known phobias, the most common being of heights, solitude, dirt, thunder, disease, animals, birds and flying insects. The victims of these and other lesser known phobias adopt an avoidance syndrome, which enables them to carry on a normal lifestyle without any great inconvenience in the main. Naturally there are a few people who carry things to excess such as refusing to ever enter a house where there may be a dog, cat or bird as a pet, or refusing to visit a sick relative either at home or in hospital for fear of 'catching' whatever they are suffering from. There could be so many examples given, but we do not need to dwell on these.

Given some thought, one can become phobic about literally anything in this life, but the majority of people usually manage to keep things in perspective and do not let this type of problem get out of hand.

These types of phobia respond very well to behaviourist treatment by a psychologist.

Other common phobias include fear of the following: Animals, Zoophobia; Birds, Ornithophobia; Blood, Haematophobia; Blushing, Ereuthophobia; Cats, Ailurophobia; Choking, Pnigophobia; Crowds, Ochlophobia; Darkness, Nyctophobia; Dust, Amathophobia; Feathers, Pteronophobia; Flying, Aerophobia; Germs, Spermophobia; Heights, Acrophobia; Lightning, Astrapophobia; Sex, Genophobia; Spiders, Arachnophobia; Thunder, Keraunophobia; Vomiting, Emetophobia.

OBSESSIONS

Very occasionally a phobic sufferer may develop an obsession.

This is an emotional disorder in which the victim cannot rid himself of an idea or an impulse, even though he knows that it begins to dominate thoughts to the exclusion of all else. This obviously leads to great disharmony in the household and interferes with general everyday living. It becomes a compulsion to wash the hands as many as fifty times a day (just because, say, the doorknob has been touched); to strip off all clothing and change from the skin out because of having sat in a chair after someone else; to scrub and clean the entire house twice or three times a day because of some imagined 'dirt'. These are just three examples of obsessional cleanliness but there are so many other types of indecision and impulse: the business man who cannot leave his office without checking absolutely everything, even though his subordinates have already done so, who cannot get into his car unless it is parked at the same particular angle in the parking lot, keys must be taken out of precisely the same pocket etc. . . . and all this before he even attempts to drive the car away!

One could quote so many instances of obsessive behaviour ranging from the small child who deliberately avoids stepping on certain paving stones right through to the adult who spoils his quality of life due to compulsive obsessions, but the list would be endless.

Obsessional people, similarly to phobics, are usually found to be highly intelligent and they find it incomprehensible that they are victims of their own compulsions.

Obsessional behaviour can also be helped greatly through sessions with a psychiatrist or psychologist well-versed in behaviour therapy (see p. 00).

2 · UNDERSTANDING ANXIETY AND FEAR

Your doctor may use various terms to describe your condition — anxiety state, tension state, anxiety reaction, stress response, among many others. What he means is that you are suffering from a nervous condition of anxiety and tension, not that you have had a nervous breakdown. Usually your symptoms follow stresses and strains in your everyday life and your doctor will try to discover what these are. Saying that your symptoms are nervous in origin does not mean that your doctor is implying that they are imaginary. He knows they are real enough, but he is saying that they are caused by nervous worry and tension, not by a bodily disease such as heart problems or kidney troubles.

WHAT IS ANXIETY?

Anxiety is an emotion very similar to fear and worry and most people do not distinguish clearly between them. Feelings of anxiety are accompanied by a whole series of changes in the body which prepare it to deal with any emergency. If the emergency mechanism gets out of hand, symptoms of anxiety become troublesome. People vary in their tendency to feel anxious. Some

25

are calm under all but the most stressful circumstances, whereas others are worried by every trivial upset and life is a great trial to them. The latter are the people who magnify every difficulty, plan in detail in advance and worry that everything will go wrong. Every setback is a major crisis, reducing them to a state of panic. Most people are between these two extremes, usually managing quite well although some things make them anxious. But when there is a major upset, or minor upsets gradually mount up, at last comes the straw that breaks the camel's back and the person becomes panicky, worried and unable to manage. He or she develops an anxiety state.

Anxiety is also common in other nervous conditions. For example, some people suffering from depression get very panicky at times. Some physical illnesses produce a lot of anxiety; patients who have had a heart attack, or whose breathing becomes difficult, become very anxious for understandable reasons. No two patients have identical symptoms. Some patients are more bothered by the psychological feelings of anxiety, some find the bodily symptoms which they experience more disturbing.

PSYCHOLOGICAL SYMPTOMS

The main psychological feeling is one of apprehension that something unspeakable is going to happen. There is a heavy sense of dread, all the more intolerable because of its vagueness. The uneasiness is present all the time but it varies in intensity from day to day and throughout any one day. Many sufferers become irritable and snap at members of their families. The anxiety interferes with attention and concentration.

One psychological symptom is particularly strange and upsetting — the curious feeling of detachment from the environment. Sounds appear to come from a long way off, everything seems to have a haze in front of it, and your body does not seem to belong to you. In extreme instances, the patient feels as if he is floating in the air looking down at himself. This condition has the technical term 'depersonalisation' or 'unreality' and it is quite common. It is a sign that the anxiety has interfered with the normal powers of perception and does not mean that the person's mind is breaking down.

BODILY SYMPTOMS

The bodily changes caused by anxiety affect many systems in the body and produce a wide variety of symptoms. Among the most common are heart complaints, such as palpitations or a feeling that the heart will stop. Giddiness, faintness, weakness or unsteadiness may also occur. Many cases of pain in the chest are the result of harmless, if uncomfortable, nervous spasms in the muscles of the rib cage, not a serious 'heart attack'. There is often difficulty in swallowing and a 'lump' in the throat. Breathing may also appear to be difficult. The patient feels that he cannot catch his breath and will suffocate. Overbreathing may produce pins and needles in the fingers because it alters the composition of gases in the blood and hence nerve function. Nausea is common; loss of appetite and diarrhoea affect some individuals. A feeling of gas around the heart or of distension may occur. Trembling can be extreme, not only of the hands but also of the feet and head. When it affects the voice-box muscles, speaking becomes difficult. The patient often tires easily and feels fatigue at the end of the day. Various aches and pains are due to excessive tension in the muscles. The commonest example is a tension headache arising from sustained nervous tension in the muscles of the scalp and the back of the neck. Many patients are understandably distressed by, and even terrified of, these bodily symptoms, fearing that they have something seriously wrong with them. However, symptoms like palpitations, diarrhoea and trembling are not caused by any disease in the organs themselves. (See also p. 00).

DEALING WITH ANXIETY

Anxiety, as an emotion, is of course known to us all. Perhaps one in every ten adults sees his or her doctor during the course of a year with symptoms of anxiety, tension or anxiety-related physical symptoms. It is thus one of the commonest illnesses. Anxiety is seen in young children, adolescents, young and middle-aged people and the elderly.

MEDICATION

Tablets lessen anxiety and make the patient more comfortable. However, in chronic anxiety states, people often find that they cannot do without drugs, not because they are addicted to them but because their anxiety symptoms return if the drugs are stopped. In these patients, the tablets keep the symptoms under control but do not 'cure' the anxiety illness in the way that penicillin cures pneumonia. Like most drugs, these tablets have side effects, mainly fatigue, drowsiness and dizziness. These are signs that the dose level is slightly too high, and your doctor will adjust it. There are very few patients for whom the right balance of control of symptoms with absence of sleepiness cannot be found. Some patients who suffer from insomnia find it helpful to take their tablets before going to bed because there is then an immediate sleep-inducing effect together with control of anxiety the following day. All medicines interact with alcohol, increasing its effect and making people drunk very easily. Alcohol should be taken *very* sparingly and cautiously and *never* if you are going to drive.

Doctors do help by prescribing the sometimes necessary anti-depressants and/or tranquillisers, which are the first prop needed to help come to terms with yourself in order to deal with life as it comes each day. One of the greatest difficulties to contend with is the positively huge number of *different* pills, potions and so on, which can be offered. There is no *one* pill that will be satisfactory for every individual, thus proving that where one person has a couple of side-effects of a certain kind there may be 20 persons on the same pill who suffer either other side-effects or possibly none at all! You can only go by what your doctor prescribes. Try them for a decent period for them to get into your system, then, if you feel they are genuinely not the ones for you, go back to your doctor and ask his opinion again. Continually telephoning for repeat prescriptions is the wrong thing to do, from both sides of the fence. We know many doctors who repeat 'scripts' for literally years without checking to see whether or not the patient is really getting any benefit from them. Many people tend to think that their doctors can solve all the life-style problems which beset them; in fact they can only offer the means to 'help yourself'.

SELF-HELP

Understanding more about this common condition is the first step towards learning to cope with anxiety and fear. Do make your family familiar with the condition as well, in order to prevent the 'pull-yourself-together' attitude.

Most of us have confronted the anxiety situation for a long time. Our anxiety has stayed with us, not because we haven't really tried to overcome it but because we have worked at it the wrong way. 'Trying hard not to be anxious' in a difficult situation is self-defeating. The reason we succumbed to our anxiety the very first time was because we tried hard not to let our symptoms happen. If at that time we had said 'To hell with it; if I am going to faint, collapse, lose touch, I can't stop it anyhow, I'll take my chances' we would have not built up our conditioned responses to the situation in the first place. Some of us are reluctant to face the difficult situation because of the pain involved or because we are afraid we might do something drastic or something serious might happen if we really 'let go'. If we work with a friend, their presence alone usually lessens the dread of something happening. Because our minds and bodies temporarily function differently when we are anxious, we may believe understandably but incorrectly, that we are becoming seriously ill or 'going crazy'. As we stop fighting our anxiety, stop thinking about what may happen and connect ourselves to our surroundings, our tension level will drop and thoughts of doom and disaster will diminish.

Are tranquillisers a bane or a boon? They become a bane when you begin to feel that you simply cannot live without them, which almost amounts to addiction, or a boon when used for just a short period to help you overcome or come to terms with a particularly problematic situation.

What are these pills/tablets/capsules? Basically, they are

calming agents which cut down the feelings of tension, anxiety or restlessness, without actually sending the person to sleep. Misused, or by taking larger doses than necessary, they can become a sleep inducing drug: in effect they are half-sisters to sleeping pills, so there could be accident risks if you have to drive or operate dangerous machinery in the course of your work. Alcoholic drink in any form should always be avoided whilst taking tranquillisers, or indeed any pills, as it potentiates their effect.

At the commencement of treatment, and because they work on the nervous system, most of the commonly prescribed tranquillisers cause side effects such as drowsiness, dryness of the mouth, blurred vision, or even slight mental confusion. Fortunately these effects tend to disappear after a few days; however, it is still essential that care is taken to watch the dosage and not think that because three pills a day are doing you good, six pills a day will make you feel even better! This is fallacy and could cause an addict to suffer withdrawal symptoms at the end of treatment such as muscle cramps, vomiting and even convulsions. There are the few people who unfortunately give rise to so much journalistic reporting against tranquillisers in general — spreading fear to those nervously ill people who could really benefit from having a short course of mild tranquillisation to help them when necessary.

It is said that doctors all over the world prescribe billions of these pills each year to people who consult them with problems which are not really physical illness at all. The patient is hoping to be given a cure-all for stresses and strains through which he feels he is going at the time. Following the introduction of these drugs to the masses in the early 1950s, there has been proof that a great deal of help can be obtained by the proper and careful use of tranquillisers, particularly by those who are suffering from emotional illnesses such as agoraphobia or any other anxiety induced condition. It still has to be said, however, that although tranquillisers work by numbing the senses so that anxiety does not seem so intense, they do not cure the underlying problem which causes the anxiety in the first place.

30

A man who loses his job, a woman alone all day perhaps with young children to care for, a widow whose recent bereavement still causes her pain, a youngster facing examinations — all these and more go along to the doctor to seek help, and come away with a prescription for one of the enormous variety of tranquillising tablets available today. All will be helped in their own way, because they are doing something which they believe to be positive. This is good even if seen for what it is — a 'prop' for the anxious time and not something to be relied on for ever more.

There are very many people who pill-pop for years without really realising that one's system eventually gets so used to them, that effectiveness is lost through familiarity and it is only habit which keeps them chained to the feeling that they could not live without them.

I have known agoraphobes who have taken the same drugs for 20 years or more, but I wonder how many ever ask themselves whose fault this is; how many people ever ask themselves whether they, rather than the doctor, accept some of this blame?

One thing is for certain: no one should ever stop taking tranquilliser pills suddenly — this really does make one feel quite lost and brings feelings of anxiety flooding back needlessly. Start by reducing your dosage gradually after consultation with your doctor. Tell him you wish to be free from taking this constant medication of a tranquillising nature. Doctors are normally very helpful to a patient whom they see is at last trying to help himself and he may suggest a prescription of a very much milder type than the one you have been used to, just to tide you over the 'weaning off' period.

Alwyn tells us: I used to take 16 tranquillisers a day for nearly five years as my then doctor told me it was the only treatment he could give me. However, on his retirement and the advent of a new young doctor to the practice, my life changed — he sat down and discussed a programme of weaning off and relaxation, no matter how hard it was going to be. At the end of six months I was 'off' pills and back at work without the thousand panics I'd been having in the past, probably through the doped up state my body had got used to. So I say to anyone who honestly wants to give up their pills — give yourself plenty to do whilst you are giving up, to prevent having symptoms that don't really exist and give it your best shot. There is no doubt you will succeed if you want to.

Peter tells us: After two years of being completely dependent on drugs and alcohol, a lethal mixture I felt at the time to be the answer to all my problems, a car accident (my fault) took my licence away from me and my marriage began to break up. Only then did I realise what a mess my life had become . . . My first step towards sanity was to put myself in the hands of a very good doctor, who also encouraged me to join an alcoholics society . . . Thank God most of the worst is behind me now and I am back at work, dependent on neither drugs nor drink. My new found sobriety enabled me to take a long hard look at myself and recognise my weaknesses . . . I endeavoured to get a balance back into my life by refusing to worry unnecessarily over trifles. This stopped the flow of adrenalin which prompted my anxieties and increased my phobic fears. If I felt tense, I just let myself go. I became stronger mentally as my mind was no longer numbed with drugs and drink, and my family relationships became happier than ever I believed possible.

Sharon tells us: Having taken tranquillisers and anti-depressants for more than three years because of agoraphobia, I began to realise my problems were not really diminishing and I was losing faith in my 'treatment'. My turning point came when I found a book on relaxation, so I determined to teach myself this. I know that there is no use waiting for someone to come along with a 'miracle' cure, as there is no such thing. Relaxation brought great relief to me and gave me motivation to recover fully.

Quick quote from a Psychiatrist
The trouble with tranquillisers is that you find yourself being nice to people you don't like!

The only 'miracle' which will actually cure anxiety is the right solution to each individual's problem — be it marital, financial, related to children or the home environment etc. — then and only then will you feel that life is that much brighter. Only by facing whatever the problem is, talking it over with someone else or even looking at it squarely alone, can it be dealt with. If it absolutely cannot be dealt with satisfactorily then you have to learn to live with it or around it and make the best of things within your own sphere — always with the hope that the sphere can be enlarged as time goes on.

Remember   A turtle doesn't move an inch until it sticks its neck out!

A PSYCHIATRIST TELLS US ABOUT TREATMENT

You may wonder how I tackle the treatment of agoraphobia. Here are a few broad principles. Firstly, I don't think that agoraphobia is a specific phobia like the ones people get about spiders or snakes. I see it more as a severe loss of confidence so that anything which raises the anxiety level, even a bit, like crossing the road or going into a lift, can provoke an attack of panic. You will always find that people with agoraphobia have fears of all kinds of situations.

There seem to be two broad groups who suffer in this way. A small group have had a serious lack of self-confidence since early childhood and these are the hardest to treat. Obviously there must be some innate variation in self-confidence in humans and someone has to be at the lower end of the scale. Then, some parents 'present' the world as a very frightening place, constantly admonishing their children to avoid danger — this must have an effect on a child's self-confidence. Thirdly, one needs a bit of luck in growing up — especially in avoiding infantile separation because, for example, of mother's illness, or even death, or admission to hospital. These are some of the causes of poor self-confidence in the smaller group and these people won't be helped much by medication — they need psychotherapy.

The much larger group of people who get agoraphobia are those who suddenly become smitten by panic in what appears to be a reasonably normal life. In these people there is always a depressive illness to cause the loss of confidence which usually suddenly becomes apparent in one of the situations people know so well. The treatment of these people is much simpler, *viz*, antidepressant treatment to get rid of the basic cause of the depression if possible (but often it has already gone — e.g. operations, virus infections, bereavement etc.) then treatment of the loss of confidence along the lines of behaviour therapy — by tackling problems in small increments.

FEARS

All patients have deep worries about their symptoms, and anxious patients are no exception. It has been found that the commonest fear is of dying during an acute panic attack. The palpitations, throbbing, flushing, shortness of breath and choking are so terrifying that feelings of impending disaster are fully understandable. In fact, people never die in a panic attack unless the person has had a previous history of a heart condition and the bodily changes are no more extreme than those occurring during hard exercise or sport. The body can easily withstand the strain. In short, anxious people are about as physically healthy as calm people.

Another unspoken fear is of going mad. Such a development never occurs. Fear of losing self-control is also common but complete breakdown is very uncommon, even when the patient feels that he is at the end of his tether.

One of the biggest worries expressed by agoraphobic people is the feeling of unreality which is so difficult to describe and which non-sufferers find so difficult to understand. 'It's just a neurotic symptom,' said one psychiatrist I questioned, but he was unable to explain further.

Most of us understand the description of agoraphobia as 'fear of the fear' but quite often it is not fear in the first place that bugs us but the dreadful nightmare sensation of almost literally 'losing one's mind'. This doesn't mean that we have become suddenly insane but that — just as one feels when waking in a different bed in strange surroundings — we are disorientated. The mind has somehow slipped out of gear and we cannot for the moment get it back.

This is where fear starts, as the sufferer struggles to adjust and fights to get back to normal. People react in many different ways. I used to find that my first reaction was to run — in any direction and as fast as I could. I found though that this just made me feel much worse. Some folk lose control completely and get hysterical. Unfortunately this always has a disastrous effect as the sufferer is likely to end up in hospital, by which time the panic has subsided — they are back to normal and left feeling foolish.

On the whole agoraphobics do not lose control. They have a dread of making a spectacle of themselves and even when having to admit feeling unwell or having to ask for a glass of water they wouldn't dream of announcing 'It's my agoraphobia', but would rather make any other excuse. What makes the feeling of unreality so frightening is the suddenness with which it can strike. The following are examples:

'I was walking along the High Street, happily window-shopping and suddenly the reflection in the shop window belonged to a stranger. I panicked and screamed . . . this episode has haunted me ever since.'

'Someone switched on a light . . . and I didn't know where I was.'

'It was just like being in a nightmare. I started to run but I felt I was in a slow-moving film and not making any progress.'

'I found myself thinking that if I walked into the road and under a bus I wouldn't feel anything.'

So often the sufferer cannot find any reason for the suddenness of the attack. Afterwards, of course, one expects the feeling and calls it down on oneself.

People going through an acute phase of anxiety find that many things trigger off feelings of unreality, particularly a sudden noise or something unexpected happening. I remember myself going through some bad patches when a raised voice would send me into a flat spin, and even turning round quickly would have the same effect.

One of the most difficult lessons that agoraphobics have to learn

— and many cannot for a long time come to terms with it — is that one can learn to control fear, through drugs, relaxation, practice; but the reason for fear — the unreality — lingers on. We have to learn that in many cases the unreality triggers off the fear and not the reverse as we are so often told.

It is possible eventually to look unreality in the face and not build up fear and panic. It is unpleasant, yes, but after a while it affects one as little as a fit of sneezing — and who worries about that (except, of course, a 'sneeze-phobic'). And in the end it goes. It takes time but it really does go. The big danger with many agoraphobics is that they stop trying and become thoroughly demoralised. Never stop. Always push yourself a bit further than you feel you can manage, and don't listen to other sufferers who suggest you sit at home and wait for it to disappear. It won't: you have got to keep going. Let us look at some ways we can help ourselves.

DEALING WITH FEAR

You must learn to allow fear to arise and accept that you have a problem. When you enter a difficult situation, expect that you are going to become frightened and get physical reactions, whatever they may be in your case . . . rapid heartbeat, difficulty in breathing, butterflies in the stomach, weak legs, sweating hands, blurry eyes, dizziness, lightheadedness etc. 'It is simply that old memory playing tricks again' . . . it is in fact your past experiences that automatically trigger your physical feelings. It is your thoughts about what you imagine is going to happen that make your physical and mental reactions get worse and accelerate. Try to recognise these negative thoughts when they start to come and then change them. Substitute more realistic thoughts for the negative ones. This is difficult to do and takes some working on, but with practice it can be done.

When fear does arise you must learn to control it. It is very difficult to do but can be accomplished with practice. When you find your fear level rising . . . stop . . . *wait* and try not to run out or rush back to your place of comfort. Expose yourself to the fear little by little and stay with it. Remember that anxious people have a fear of the *fear* itself!

Each individual has to find his own ways to handle his fear in particular situations. Here are some examples of what some people have done to keep fear levels manageable. One persons sings when he is driving his car. The sound of his voice is a comfort to him. Another person tells himself 'I will just let it be. I won't fight it, let the feelings come — they are only feelings. I am not going to faint; I haven't done so yet; even if I do, so what?' Another person keeps a picture of his family on the dashboard of his car. When he finds the feeling coming on he quickly glances at the picture and asks himself, 'What is so different about sitting here in my car from sitting at home in the living room?'

Also to touch familiar objects, to see and recognise familiar things helps to bring the fear level down.

If you try to eliminate the fear altogether you are fighting it and not letting it be. If you can accept and let it be it will decrease. Learning that you can do things to bring your fear level down is the first step to being able to cope in the phobic situation.

A DOCTOR ASKS, 'ARE YOU A VICTIM OF A.W.T.?'

Every day finds thousands of people in hospitals or their doctor's surgery because of A.W.T. You won't find it written on any doctor's list but, believe me, it is a real problem. A.W.T. stands for Anxiety, Worry and Tension, and you would be amazed how much trouble it can cause. For instance, you don't have to be told when someone is worried — his face may be white, his brow will be furrowed, his mouth is tight and his teeth clenched. This is all because his worried mind has sent a signal to the gland which produces adrenalin, and adrenalin produces muscle-tightness which, in turn, causes pain — a sort of chain reaction.

Usually the first places to feel tension are the muscles in the stomach and at the back of the neck. Take Mr G. He complained of stomach pain most of the time and although checks showed he didn't have an ulcer, he was sure he did. I learned he was worried about his job and also that he'd noticed every time he went fishing the pain disappeared! You see, on the riverbank he was relaxed. In other words his A.W.T. vanished and so did the stomach muscle cramps.

In many cases headaches too are caused by A.W.T. Blood vessels inside the skull are squeezed down so hard by nervous tension it produces blinding pain.

A.W.T. can even cause skin trouble. What happens is this: each time you are upset, blood vessels in the skin react by squeezing out a fluid into the skin tissues. Eventually the fluid is forced on to the surface of the skin where it becomes scaly, crusty and itchy. It is called neurodermatitis.

Have you ever had a narrow escape in a car? Your heart pounds, you gulp deep breaths, you feel faint. That's all due to fear, but more insidious fear caused by A.W.T. can lead to other symptoms — including pain in the chest.

There are three types of people prone to the effects of A.W.T. First, those who are pessimists by nature and who never look on the bright side. Then, there is the perpetual worrier. Quite a few women fall into this category — if there's nothing to fret about close to home, sure enough they will find something to worry about elsewhere.

There are also some folk who at some stage convince themselves things have just got too much for them. I have come across people whose misfortunes make the burdens of some A.W.T. victims seem small indeed yet *they* can bounce back with a determined smile on their face. You see, they have got the right mental attitude to life.

Can we avoid A.W.T? Well, here are some tips to stop it harming you: don't keep worrying yourself and analysing every ache or pain; looking for trouble is the best way of finding it! Learn to like your work; most jobs have some good points; find them and you will cut out an awful lot of tension. Have a hobby when you feel tense it can work wonders to relax for half a minute thinking about that bookcase you are making, that coming weekend, those seedlings you are growing in the greenhouse. Try

38

to be more tolerant and learn to like people. Bearing grudges can have disastrous effects on your health. Get into the habit of looking for something cheerful to say — people will like you for it and you will like yourself a lot more too. Don't let problems hang around: decide what you're going to do, do it, then put it out of your mind. Believe me, if you bear these in mind you'll not only live longer — you'll enjoy life better.

There is nothing either good or bad, but thinking makes it so.

Hamlet

I am indebted to a friend, who wishes to remain anonymous, for the following:

Do not force the pace of life though much you have to do,
Take some time for being quiet, just a minute, maybe two.
To make a break from all that drives you on from day to day
Give yourself a chance to stop, to think, perhaps to pray.
You need to soothe the jangled nerves and calm the worried mind,
To ease the overburdened heart, to rest and to unwind,
Find a peace within yourself and stronger you will be
Having learned the precious secret of serenity.

THE BIOLOGY OF FEAR

Are your nerves calm and peaceful today or do they seem to be on edge so that everything upsets you? Are you saying that they will not let you sit still for a moment, or do you merely tell you doctor in a plaintive manner that you are 'so nervous'? These are common complaints, but if you do say any of these things or if you fondly believe that you are of a nervous temperament, prepare yourself for a shock. There is nothing the matter with your nerves: the trouble is elsewhere.

Let us examine the nerves: we find that each one is a thread of living tissue and that these little fibres connect the brain cells with virtually every cell in the body. Each one consists of a central core surrounded by a membrane. They resemble the electric wires in your telephone or radio, except that they are composed of soft tissue instead of metal. Some of these nerves carry impulses from the brain to the various organs and tissues, while others carry messages from these to the great central office. The nerves are only a means of communication: they do not govern anything. Since they only carry messages in one direction or another it is wrong to speak of these conditions of which you are complaining as 'nervous'.

To find the source of so-called 'nervous' troubles we must trace back from the nerves to the brain, and then to that unseen worker within — the mind — which presides over the brain and uses the wonderful mechanism of the nervous system to control the body. We must realise that any so-called nervous condition, from the simplest case of fidgets to pronounced hysteria, is caused by a state of mind that is interfering with the orderly control of the affairs of the body. If we understand this point we shall at once see how to deal with these conditions. Your hand trembles and you say that you are nervous. For some reason you are not exercising a normal control over the muscles. There is a state of indecision behind this phenomenon, and this state is in the mind. In other words, so-called nervousness is a partial loss of control or an irregular control in the central office. When this becomes complete we have the condition known as hysteria. We may know people who become hysterical on the slightest provocation. They simply let their feelings take charge of them and give up all self-control.

This, then, gives us a clue. Let us follow it further. We know that most of the functions of the body are carried on by the subconscious: so it is there that we must look for the real cause of the trouble. This part of the mind ordinarily works calmly and methodically, but if it is upset it becomes erratic in its action. It then behaves just as though it did not know exactly what to do and the results of this indecision are seen in the outer behaviour. It may give us trembling of the body, a case of indigestion, irregular heart action or some other condition that we wrongly call nervous. If you can imagine a train dispatcher sending a rapid succession of contradictory orders over the wires you can see what would

40

happen. Traffic would be disrupted. At places it would stop entirely, for engineers would refuse to move until the controller made up his mind what he wanted done. Your stomach or some other organ behaves in just this way if you allow a similar condition to possess you. The cells of your stomach are accustomed to obeying orders. If the directions cannot be understood, digestion may stop entirely and then you blame your nerves.

We know definitely the things that will interfere with the normal action of the subconscious. Any negative state of mind such as a strong dislike, a buried hatred, a habit of condemning others, some little tolerance will have this result. So will a feeling that one has been unjustly dealt with, for this will induce condemnation. Fear acts thus, of course, and since all these negative thoughts are founded on fear we may say that fear — known or unknown — is the cause of the trouble. You may mention worry. Worry is an expression of fear and a very common one: so our rule holds. We find that most nervous patients are victims of worry because they fear a panic attack. All these fears and negative thoughts may have been acquired through years of wrong thinking, or they may be suggestions from others that the mind has accepted which is very apt to be the case with nervous children. So it comes to this: if you are nervous or if you think that your nerves are on edge and that you are ready to fly to pieces you are really afraid of something. Your fear of reaction to things, people or conditions starts the train of negative emotions that upsets your subconscious and so causes your troubles.

THE REMEDY

What will you do for your case of 'nerves'? Medicine is powerless to cure these conditions. Sedative drugs relieve the symptoms but only by putting the mechanism partially to sleep — they do not get at the cause: the conducting apparatus gets the treatment, and this is not at fault. Besides, if over-strong drugs are used or if they are relied upon exclusively a habit may be formed that will be difficult to break. We must get back to the cause.

In recognition of the fact that the real trouble is mental, many forms of psychotherapy have been devised — some of which have shown fair results, but I believe that the best treatment of all is a generous dose of *truth*, to be repeated until the habit of correct thinking is well established. In this way we establish control of all things on a firm basis and the trouble will not return unless the patient returns to his old habit of thought. The minute you begin to think weakly because you fear that you cannot overcome the problem before you, all the old fears have their opportunity to attack you, and they make the most of it. Train yourself to think strong and they will scurry away. The lesson is obvious: attend to your thoughts. If you let them run riot they will stir the subconscious into erratic action and you will be, as you say, 'very nervous'. You must change your thoughts or they will manage you.

Fear never robs tomorrow of sorrow: it robs today of strength

A PSYCHOTHERAPIST TELLS US ABOUT TRUTH

We all know that facing truth is important. O.K., so I will give you all truth. Get up off your backsides and live! That's truth. Have you gone and done it? I'll bet not. These things are easy to say, hard to put into practice. If you bite your nails you know you will have lovely nails if only you will stop. So, O.K. stop. Have you stopped, then?

There is a strong theory that the parasympathetic nervous system opposes the sympathetic nervous system. The sympathetic produces the flight/fight anxiety, the parasympathetic calmness, and they can't both dominate together. So, in theory, if you relax you cannot have anxiety feelings. Whatever anyone thinks or says you have to take into account several things if you really want to break anxiety patterns. You have three inner bits of you to reconcile, and dealing with only one bit leaves the other two to fight back and defeat you. These three bits in simple language are the unconscious self, the conscious self and the body-doing (or motor) self. That is why behaviour therapy without work on the mind does not always work so well and analysis of thoughts and feelings without body-doing work is the same. Once you have found the unconscious drives within you and reconciled these consciously, then you've also got to practise actually doing new things with your body.

Why can't you analyse yourself? Because you cannot see your own behaviour patterns. That's the first truth to face. You are not behaving the way you think you are. Take a hypothetical case: a husband and wife come in complaining that the wife is scared to go out and face people. They both blame her strongly. It only takes two minutes to find her unconscious is scared to death of a husband who is so critical towards her he is actually cruel. Yet consciously she sees him as helping her with the housework and shopping, so he's a martyr. He also sees himself as a martyr, being driven towards his own breakdown by her constant weeping and moaning. Between them they have placed him on a pedestal as a superior being and she feels terribly inferior. Is it any wonder she also feels inferior in her life generally? Probably the therapist will also find the wife has a sad childhood history. But what is the truth? The first thing is that it is the husband who is the weak one. He's so weak he's scared to allow his wife to become an equal person in case it exposes his own feared weaknesses. And the wife plays his game because her unconscious senses what would happen if she grew strong and her strength frightened him. The marriage might break up and she would lose her own security.

Neither of them will see how they actually behave without professional help. His overt behaviour is very solicitous to his wife and hers is gratitude for all he does. Get him to see himself on video tape and it will scare the life out of him, the same way as listening to your own voice on tape for the first time will do. Ask her to verbalise her real repressed hatred of his constant criticism and she will be scared to put it into words. Can you analyse yourself and your behaviour this way? No. And when they know what is happening will they change overnight? No. They've been

43

behaving this way maybe ten or twenty years. They have to feel their way gradually with new behaviour patterns.

Incidentally, if you are talking truth, don't waste your sympathies on the wife either. The truth is, if she really wants to be well no one makes her carry around today the past traumas of her childhood, and if she hasn't got the guts to take the chance to be independent it is she who has *decided* to remain with such a husband.

Are you all really ready to face *truth* now? Mention to an agoraphobic woman the possibility that maybe she is retreating from placing herself in situations where she might encourage more sexual advances and, therefore, that she is really scared of acknowledging her own sexuality and she will run from you shouting how monstrous of you to suggest it. Truth says that it may be a distinct possibility.

Behaviour is a mirror in which everyone shows his image

3 · DEPRESSION

It is a fact that 70% of agoraphobic people become depressed at some time or another during the period of their illness. Did you know that there are several different types of depression?

Depression is a very common problem and you are certainly not alone with yours. Women are more prone to fits of depression than men, probably because of their biological make up. Many people who feel low and depressed are reluctant to seek help and there are a number of reasons why this is so. Indeed many are reluctant to speak of their condition and may successfully hide it and put on a good face for friends and neighbours, and in particular their families. Many people are actually unable to express in words exactly the way they feel.

The idea of going mad and, in consequence, of being locked up is another common and deep-seated fear which often prevents nervous people seeking the help they need. Depression is not a form of madness but a matter of misinterpreting feelings and happenings. People suffering from depression are usually conscientious and hard-working folk — in fact, the cream of society. Although you may well feel inferior and utterly useless now, any sense of innate worthlessness is just another symptom of the illness. In fact, it is well-known that depression without any treatment whatsoever does eventually lift although it is very hard to envisage at the time.

In a debilitating stage of your depression make no snap decisions. Such acts should be avoided at this time. Be patient for a short while and you will find that things look very different as you move back into a happier frame of mind. You will then be able to make sound decisions on your own problems.

Some persons may feel along with agoraphobia they experience levels of deep to mild depression. Some of the depression is felt to be connected with their 'frustrated state'. How much of the depression is actually related to their being agoraphobic? Depression is a state in which the person is feeling helpless and hopeless about ever being able to achieve important personal goals; he then begins to feel incapable, useless and worthless to a markedly unreasonable degree and disinclined to do necessary things.

There are degrees to which a person feels depressed. These range from feelings of fatigue and unhappiness to suicidal inclinations and near-paralysis. Every human being must experience periods of depression in the real world although usually these are brief and non-disruptive. The more severe degrees of depression are usually the product of overwhelming, unrealistically negative thoughts, expectations and beliefs.

Being agoraphobic implies repeated inability despite much effort to reach goals that others attain readily. Therefore, some degree of depression inevitably accompanies being agoraphobic. With in-depth thought and determination most persons are able to fight their agoraphobia and the depression lifts, the black clouds fade and feelings of self-esteem and worth take their place.

Today only a very small number of depressed persons need to be referred to a psychiatrist. Many people do not like this idea. This is where self-help can be most useful, and with determination can be very successful.

There are many causes of depression. In most cases a complete medical examination is indicated at the initial stage to dismiss organic disease. The housewife who finds it increasingly difficult to cope may have some other illness like anaemia or diabetes of which she is unaware — this needs to be checked out. Depression sometimes comes on after influenza or glandular fever. It may be caused by side-effects of tablets the patient is taking at the time for blood pressure, or even by the contraceptive pill. One of the reasons for depression being more common among women than men is that women have a more complicated hormonal system. The mechanism which regulates the menstrual cycle or the changes which occur during pregnancy and after childbirth and the symptoms which occur when menstruation finally ceases, all of these things are dependent on the harmonious workings of many glands in the body. If one of these organs over reacts or under reacts it can upset the delicate balance and become a basis for depression.

Every function of the body involves a chemical process, whether it is physical or mental activity, even just breathing and feeling. When we get sick we are suffering from a metabolic upset, a chemical imbalance. The brain is especially susceptible to changes in body chemistry and yet many psychiatrists do not think enough about the 'whole' person and the physical state of the patient. The old saying 'You are what you eat' is not precisely true although every function of the body and especially mental activity is dependent upon the quality and kind of food we eat. Our genetic endowment plays a fundamental part in mental health and some persons may become mentally disorientated when they eat or lack certain foods. Most people believe that there are frequently important deficiencies in necessary nutritional elements: this is particularly so in the emotionally ill. It should be said that this theory is not strictly accepted by all in the medical profession as it certainly has not been satisfactorily proved.

TYPES OF DEPRESSION

Apart from the depression which follows a physical condition such as influenza, the birth of a child, or that which occurs at the change of life, there are two main types of depression. The first is brought on by adverse circumstances and the second is causeless depression.

The most common cause of depression is an adverse environment. For example, the reason for her unhappiness is obvious to the mother of a severely handicapped child as she wonders what the future will hold for him and who will look after him when she is not there. Or there may be some terrible catastrophe such as a member of the family being killed in a car accident. Faced with disaster we all need the support and help of family and friends, and perhaps also of the doctor. The person who is uncertain about the cause of the trouble needs expert help to identify the problem. For example, if you hold the printed page close to your eyes you will not be able to read anything, but move the book back a few inches and all becomes clear. It is much the same with some of our problems — we often live too close to them to appreciate their true significance. The above could be identified as reactive depression.

A depression without apparent cause is called endogenous depression. Out of the blue, for no obvious reason, a person become wretched and miserable; this is occasionally preceded by a period of elation, during which stage of excitement the victim feels on top of the world, completely tireless, and constantly on the go and talking non-stop. Endogenous depression is not so common as the reactive, environmental type above.

This division into reactive and endogenous depression is an over-simplification of a complex situation. With a depression brought on by adverse circumstances the stress sometimes becomes too great and the depression which then emerges can be indistinguishable from an endogenous depression. Imagine, for example, a woman under considerable strain after her husband's heart attack. She learned to cope, carrying on with her housework and running the family business which had been her husband's occupation, but was completely devastated when he suddenly died and was quite unable to accept his death. She developed all sorts of strange ideas and accused him of deserting her. She was given treatment for endogenous depression and after a few weeks was able to face life again and run the family business on her own. She has never relapsed.

DEALING WITH DEPRESSION

The stresses caused by an adverse environment may well be eased by discussing the problem with the family doctor. Just occasionally the difficulty may be sorted out and cleared up but more often than not the person has to learn to come to terms with her problem. On her own a woman may feel that the situation is unbearable and the intervention of someone else can sometimes clear the air and make tolerable a heavy burden. What the patient needs is physical treatment but she still needs encouragement and moral support from her doctor and family until recovery is well established. For her part the patient must co-operate with her doctor and family. She must learn to understand her illness and to appreciate what is being done for her.

The first treatment for depression is usually given in the form of tablets from your doctor. If these are taken as prescribed they can lift the depression in a matter of ten days. The patient should be completely back to normal after a short time but the tablets do not act immediately and the patient must be prepared to persevere. Adequate levels of the drug have to be built up in the blood and other tissues before the patient begins to feel better. Some of the tablets have troublesome side effects and with others there are important dietary restrictions. It may mean giving up alcohol for the time being, and avoiding cheese and various foods which your doctor will list for you. You should always ask your doctor, if offered a new tablet, whether there are any restrictions — he will respect you more if you show intelligent interest. If the tablets upset you by all means tell your doctor how you feel but you must not stop taking them or change the dose without his advice. Once the drug has started to work the effect should be dramatic. One patient asked how it was possible for a few tablets to alter her whole attitude to life and make her feel so much better.

POST-NATAL DEPRESSION

Depression after childbirth is not a new disease, nor is it confined to our culture. As long ago as the 4th century B.C. Hippocrates described a woman who was experiencing severe insomnia, restlessness and difficulties after giving birth to twins. At its mildest, post-natal depression is the emotional low, usually called the 'blues' that hits some 80% of women after giving birth. It is not at all unusual for a husband to turn up at visiting times to find the entire ward in floods of tears, often about a trivial event. The point is that the 'blues' are transient, brief and self-limiting; most women are over them by the tenth day. On the other hand some women find it lasts much longer, a small percentage having a full blown depressive attack with tiredness, lethargy, anxiety and feelings of inadequacy, irritability, sleep problems, loss of appetite or over-eating and lack of interest in sex. So what causes post-natal depression? The short answer is — no one really knows. Everyone agrees that pregnancy and birth are times of great physical and emotional upheaval but whether the depression is psychological in origin or whether it is caused by hormones no one seems quite sure. The first thing to do is recognise that you have it, which is not always easy, but it is essential to have a talk with your doctor or health worker and hope that she can help you over the bad patch. Alternatively, try to discover from the baby clinic other mothers who are also experiencing the same symptoms and have a good talk with them. Obviously there are very many women who will not experience any of these things mentioned above and will sail through the whole thing without any problems of any kind!

More and more patients go to see their doctor with their own diagnosis of depression. Depression covers an enormous variety of emotional states and means different things to different people. It has thus become a rather meaningless term. And a dangerous one too. Not infrequently depression is a cover-up for various social and psychological conditions. It is easier to label a patient's despair about appalling housing conditions as depressive illness than to move a housing department to action. It is easier to suffer from depression than confront a difficult family situation. In this way the confrontation can be postponed — unfortunately at the expense of the 'depressed' person.

People who say they are depressed often provoke anger, frustration, boredom, rejection and so on. These are very real feelings and in part reflect what goes on in the patient. Depression is an interactional process: it is difficult to remain permanently depressed without the collusion of others. Family, friends and professionals can all become part of a depressive system that the patient creates.

Our life is what our thoughts make it — I stood yesterday, I can stand today, and I will face tomorrow.

Some case histories, with which you may identify, follow:

Suzanne writes: Here are my tips on combatting depression. If I know I'm likely to get depressed, due to, say, pre-menstrual tension, I prepare in advance by taking lots of Vitamin B complex and especially B6 (about 100 mgs daily) and ensure I eat small frequent meals to keep my blood sugar levels up. I steer clear of coffee, tea and alcohol as they aggravate the condition. I drink decaffeinated coffee and fruit juices — much healthier anyway. However, if the blues just descend without warning I find listening to a lively piece of music — the louder and livelier the better — really does lift that grey feeling. I pamper myself by spending at least half an hour making up my face and washing and styling my hair. I phone an old friend I've not seen for ages and have a good, long chat, then I turn out all my drawers and sort through my old mementoes. I find the concentration required takes my mind off my depression totally. However, my really great tip is: be nice to yourself. Treat yourself to whatever you know you like best, even if it means breaking a diet by indulging in a certain doughnut. Go ahead — it works wonders.

Mrs R. tells us: There was a time seven months ago when I felt that life was not worth living and I carefully planned that I would collect enough tablets to create a large dose, sufficient to end it all. Oh yes, I knew what I was doing (or so I thought) just as if I was a General planning to end a battle. Then one afternoon I received a telephone call from my child's school. She had wanted to hurry home to Mummy and had been knocked down in front of the school. Without another thought in my head about agoraphobia, depression or not 'being able to go out', I had my coat on and was already rushing down the road to my daughter thinking of nothing other than to comfort her and praying that her injuries were not to prove fatal. Thanks to God they weren't, but as I accompanied her in the ambulance, I vowed that life was too sweet to throw away and asked God's forgiveness for even thinking about doing away with mine and leaving my husband and child with the burden of possible guilt on their minds for all time. From that moment I have changed, thankfully, from what I thought was a guilt-ridden, useless person to a more or less happy soul who now looks forward to a happier future with my husband and the child whom I almost lost.

Mary-Ann writes: It hit me quickly and quietly with no warning, a terrifying, shattering feeling that came to alter and shape my life for seven long years. I awoke every morning with the overwhelming feeling that there was something wrong. I had another day to get through, while everyone else was going about their lives with the happy confidence that had been mine for 36 years. How I took it for granted — that I could walk up the road and say 'Hello' to my friends and neighbours, go shopping, visit friends (you lose a lot of friends when you are agoraphobic and depressed), go on holiday, attend the many school functions which are necessary when you have four children or just be alone in the house doing such simple things as having a bath, washing my hair and even hanging out the laundry. All these things which had been so simple became a major operation. Then came the depression, the feelings of guilt that I was spoiling the lives of loved ones, the children I wanted so much — now the despair of not enjoying their young tender years.

If this happens it seems so unfair that you tell yourself it would have been better to have died or to have had an illness that is obvious to everyone. No one seems to understand depression. Some even think you bring it on yourself like alcoholism or drug addiction and tell you to pull yourself together. How many times I've heard that! However, I am eternally grateful that there is a light at the end of the tunnel at last. I can walk up the road and not feel afraid and actually enjoy shopping and travelling by bus. I now look forward to a holiday free from the fears and frustrations that I endured all the other times I've been away in the past seven years. Life is becoming enjoyable once more but 'letting go' of agoraphobia and depression is hard to do. You cannot forget it and it leaves you feeling sad but wiser. It teaches you not to take life for granted, that illness and bad things can and do happen to everyone. So now I have to make up for those years of heartache, fears and depression. I am strong, I know, and can count on myself whatever happens in the future because I know that I got through this hell alone. It's the only way, for no one can do it for you.

MID-LIFE CRISIS

So many people find their agoraphobia, compounded by depression, increases, indeed even starts for the first time, during their time of menopause, in the case of women, or mid-life crisis in the case of men. A doctor writes the following for our male readers:

MALE MENOPAUSE: MYTH OR MID-LIFE REALITY?

Just before my fifty-first birthday I began to have insomnia. I was worrying about money, my health and dozens of other things. Shortly afterwards I lost interest in everything. All I wanted to do was lie around. I couldn't even read much because I had difficulty in concentrating.

I just didn't have the same enthusiasm for my work. What was wrong? Did I have a strange virus or a metabolic disorder? Was I showing early signs of a brain tumour? No. What I was suffering from, a specialist told me when I finally sought help, was the 'male menopause'.

Taken literally this phrase is ridiculous. Men don't have a menstrual cycle, nor do they lose their reproductive powers in their forties and fifties as women do. Yet many doctors use 'menopause' to describe the psychological reactions that trouble men as they age. After my doctor's diagnosis I started investigating. I found that an important study concluded that the 'mid-life transition' is a predictable stage of development all men go through. Most experience it at around 40 but others not until their fifties. For some, the transition is relatively smooth but for most men it is a time of doubt — about their work, their love relationships and their goals.

In the course of my investigations I came across two men of my acquaintance who were going through such a crisis themselves. Charles is 48 and an insurance broker. Six months ago he began worrying about his health. His father had a heart attack at 53 and Charles was certain that he had heart trouble too. 'I'd go to bed at night and my heart would start pounding,' he told me. 'My doctor said my heart was all right but I didn't believe him.' Charles began to have two or three drinks almost every night, 'To help me sleep,' he explained. He also started thinking about getting out of the insurance business: 'I've been at it 25 years now and I want to do something different.'

Ted is 53 and a successful hospital consultant. When he was 49 he went into a slump. 'I was earning a lot of money,' he said, 'but I was bored. I found I hated going to work.'

These men had some of the symptoms of the male menopause. Other indications may include insomnia and/or chronic fatigue, loss of libido, anxiety, hypochondria, loss of appetite, increased smoking or alcohol consumption, high blood pressure, migraine.

What causes the male menopause? Why do so many careers nosedive, affairs flourish, marriages fall apart? Is it a purely psychological reaction to the process of ageing and the prospect of death? Many doctors think so but we have learnt a lot about brain chemistry in recent years and we now suspect that many diseases once labelled psychological may possibly be caused by chemical alterations. What we do know about the male menopause is that there is no quick, dramatic cure for it, but that the crisis will pass. It may last for anything from several months to several years then subside as unexpectedly as it began. Realisation of this is often consoling in itself.

Here are some other things I tell my patients: Get regular, vigorous exercise, preferably every day but at least three times a week. This will give a general feeling of well-being and help counteract insomnia. Continue to work regularly at your job. A holiday may be helpful but you will probably enjoy it more a little later on. Do not make a drastic change in your life. You may reasonably want to change career but to do so now could be difficult and costly. However, most men in this situation find it satisfying to develop new interests.

Change without destroying the basic framework of your life is a sound policy for the menopausal man. Be wary of both alcohol and new women. A new woman appeals as a possible source of rejuvenation. Your wife may no longer seem exciting or young enough and you may be convinced that the answer to your problem is to leave her for someone else. But to make such a change while in the throes of the male menopause is hazardous at best. There is a very great risk that the benefits — possibly a restitution of libido and potency — will be as transitory as the illusory benefit to be gained through alcohol!

MENOPAUSAL?

Are you one of those unfortunate ladies who first experienced agoraphobia difficulties whilst in the throes of the female 'mid-life' crisis, more commonly known as the menopause? This does occasionally happen as during this time so many stresses and strains get magnified to an abnormal degree, leaving the way open to agoraphobia and depression.

No woman can escape from the menopause: it has to be faced at some time or other, usually between the late thirties to mid-fifties (a guide to the age it will happen is the ages at which menopause began for your close female relatives). It may last six months, it may last three years or even more.

Ignorance and superstitions die hard and many a woman in the past has dreaded the menopause simply because she had been told stories by her mother or grandmother that it was a time filled with alarm and despondency! Fortunately the enlightened woman of today realises that although it cannot be avoided, it can at least be faced with equanimity and forebearance and the knowledge that medical relief can be obtained to help with the 'worst parts', if any.

Every woman from the time of her teenage years knows the physiology of the 'period' during which time her system is capable, each month, of meeting the demands of pregnancy and it is the cessation of those periods on a gradual scale, when the middle years are approaching, which is termed the climacteric or menopause.

The cessation or irregularity of periods is one of the obvious signs that hormonal alterations are taking place and is a phase scarcely noticeable in the majority of women: it is only the unfortunate few who really need some help.

One of the most common complaints is 'hot flushes', a feeling of intense heat throughout the body and sometimes making the face quite rosy. It lasts only momentarily then diminishes; maybe it occurs only two or three times a day; with others it may happen as many as twenty or so times, even throughout the night causing disturbed sleep or insomnia if the supply of oestrogen is diminishing too rapidly. This is where medical help can come to the rescue with tablets which can help the hormonal balance. There are many women who prefer to be stoical, knowing that even without treatment the system will cope, readjusting over a period of time.

There are several other minor symptoms such as headaches, a feeling of 'fullness', giddiness, some discomfort in the limbs with occasional 'tingling' in the hands and feet, shrinking and dryness of the vaginal passage and perhaps insomnia.

Is it any wonder then that a woman feels 'on edge' or nervy during the menopause — particularly a woman who has been an anxious type before her middle years appear — perhaps causing her to be so tired that she starts staying in the house, 'letting herself go' a little and not caring about her appearance. It is in such fertile soil that seeds containing symptoms of agoraphobia can so easily flourish.

It is essential that the woman takes stock when she realises what is happening — if she does not realise her family or friends certainly will, *and* remark upon it! This is the time to sit down and think about improving the situation — this is where the enlistment of family or friends or both is so important, especially to help with housework, shopping and children, if any. It is no great crime for a housewife to accept help temporarily without letting it become a habit (to prevent agoraphobia getting a hold), and accept that she is a bit depleted and needs to draw breath. On the other hand she now has to prepare her plan of action and gain lost self-esteem by getting to grips with her appearance and fitness generally.

There is no excuse for not doing a few exercises (housework is exercise of a different kind) to firm those flabby muscles. Learn to breathe correctly in front of an open window: fill your lungs with fresh air and gradually begin to have a feeling of well-being. Have a new 'hair-do', try to change the way you look to satisfy *you* and please never lie abed in the mornings: it is most important to get up, shower and dress to begin each morning. Lying in bed most of the day just thinking of how miserable you are will only make things worse and bring on guilt feelings, which are so unnecessary.

Working women who have recovered or come to terms with agoraphobia carry on working if they are already employed, perhaps taking an odd day off. On the other hand, recovered agoraphobes are usually stoical enough to carry on regardless. After all, the menopause is a natural happening.

As your bodily system gradually readjusts to the changeover, naturally you will feel a great deal more like your old self together with the added bonus of knowing you can look forward with a much more relaxed attitude towards your sexual life without fear of an unwanted pregnancy.

One must emphasise that only a very small number of women actually get into such a depressed state as this: the vast majority sail through the whole thing without any great difficulty and feel like new, born-again women, starting a fresh phase in their lives more confident than ever.

Remember the old woman who said, 'I've had a lot of trouble in my time, and most of it never happened.'

Phyllis says: Having been quite severely agoraphobic for just over a year, I was approaching my 42nd birthday with a certain amount of gloom as I had an idea that the 'change' was dogging my heels having been suffering irregular periods for about seven months with a few slight headaches thrown in and a bit of a weight problem too.

Well, the birthday came and went and so did five more months when, hey presto, the periods stopped completely and have not occurred since. I was a very lucky lady as I really began to feel extraordinarily well. I decided to lose all excess weight and start going out and about again. Progress was slow, of course, at first but I felt like a million dollars by the time birthday number 43 came along as I'd even been on a super European tour with my husband with no sign of agoraphobia at all. My life really has started over!

The next time you think about your own situation at home or elsewhere, try asking yourself 'Am I alone or lonely?' . . . there is a vast difference. I feel now that many of us do not appreciate just what we *have* in the way of relationships and that we could make a vast change in our lives if we would only try.

The more one reads, listens to, learns and understands about life's anxiety provoking factors, the easier it becomes to give our problems a sense of proportion and place our priorities in the correct order. There are some people who say, 'If I read a list of symptoms I invariably find myself having them.' They forget that this works the other way round: many suffer almost unbearable agony of mind convincing themselves they have cancer or T.B. or heart trouble etc. If they would only take the trouble to read and discover the *real* symptoms of these illnesses, and believe their doctors when they are told they are not in the throes of disease, they would be less depressed, less fatigued, and more able to get on with life in general.

PRE-MENSTRUAL TENSION

This difficult state affects very many of the female population, and causes a great deal of misunderstanding in their households, particularly when they 'fly off the handle' over almost nothing at both their long suffering husbands and children too. It happens usually a week or ten days before the start of a period.

A well-known authority on women's ailments says that some

women find that when they keep a diary and note the dates of their worst panic attacks, these nearly always coincide with the start of menstruation, possibly a few days before or a few days after the first 'bleeding stage'. The whole syndrome can embrace depression, being irritable over trifles, extreme tiredness and a feeling of being 'blown up'. The doctor suggests taking meals that are small and often during the day instead of leaving yourself for long periods of time without a meal (thus lowering your blood sugar): a small snack every three hours or so throughout your working day is far better than one large meal at night.

There is a great deal of help available from your doctor. There are many drugs on the market which reduce water retention and sometimes it is as simple as this to put things right and make the woman and her family much happier once again.

Why suffer unnecessarily in these days of enlightenment? There is nothing to be ashamed of and certainly a great deal to be gained.

It should be mentioned, however, that pre-menstrual tension is not well understood by the man in the street. Mention it to many men and women and they'll say, 'It's all in the mind.' Doctors believe that P.M.T., or pre-menstrual syndrome, as they prefer it to be called, is as much an illness as, say, diabetes.

Pre-menstrual tension is both a psychological and physical disorder. Psychological symptoms are depression, irritability, lethargy, crying spells and in the worst cases, irrational and violent behaviour. Physically you can suffer with asthma, sore throats, acne, fluid retention, backache, hot flushes, nausea and dizziness. Note, however, that suffering these symptoms *doesn't* automatically mean you have P.M.T. — you only suffer this if your symptoms occur regularly at the same time before your period and disappear afterwards.

A good 60% of women never experience P.M.T. 30% have it mildly and can treat themselves by limiting their intake of fluid and salt and eating little but often. It is only the remaining 10% who require treatment, because of severe symptoms.

The treatment for P.M.T. is simple and effective, and based on the fact that P.M.T. is caused by progesterone deficiency. (The female body ceases producing this hormone during the second half of the menstrual cycle.) The cure is, therefore, to take progesterone, usually in the form of suppositories. Because it is a perfectly natural hormone, there are absolutely no harmful side-effects. Some patients have taken it for 20 years and are totally healthy.

The first thing to do if you are suspect is to chart your symptoms over a few months to establish whether they are recurring each time. Jot down on a calendar what symptoms you have on each day of the month. Your doctor should then be able to assess whether you are actually suffering from P.M.T.

Don't accept P.M.T. as something which women have to live through. I've never heard a diabetic say that!

YOU CAN'T BEAT A GOOD LAUGH

Do you know what is recommended as one of the world's finest tonics? Simply — a good laugh! Laughter, and lots of it, can really add years to your life, and what does the most good is a deep, hearty laugh, not a polite titter or a nervous cackle or even a self-conscious giggle! Every time you have a really good laugh, in a sense it gives your lungs a spring clean. It forces out the stuffy, stale air that lies deep down, lets your lungs expand and fills every last corner with good fresh oxygen. It's also good exercise for the ribcage. All in all the man who laughs a lot will have a much healthier chest than the more miserable type. He will also be less prone to troubles such as chronic bronchitis and pneumonia, and those colds won't be so liable to go to his chest.

Perhaps you didn't realise it but laughter can even clear a headache! Especially those headaches where the pain shoots up the back of your head and over the top. Why? The real cause of that headache is tension in the many tiny muscles in your scalp. Laughter relaxes them. Your tension disappears and with it your headache.

Another thing: just as your feet go flat if you do not use them, so does your face if you don't use your laughter muscles! That's why people who laugh a lot tend to look years younger. How often have you seen a grumpy face suddenly light up in laughter and immediately look youthful again? It's not laughter lines that are ageing, it's the frowning forehead, the downcast twist of the lips.

A bout of laughter can even steady your blood pressure. The man who sees humour has one of the best protections against a heart attack. The same applies to the digestive system. I'll always remember an old doctor saying an acid tongue can lead to an acid tummy — and it's rare indeed to find a cheery joker suffering from an ulcer!

Medically there are few infectious things which do you good but laughter can certainly be considered as one. It doesn't matter one bit what tickles you — if it can make you laugh then it is good for you. So don't think the doctor cracks a joke with you on his rounds of the ward or at home just because he fancies himself as a bit of a comic. No, he knows full well the valuable unwinding effect even the smallest chuckle can have . . . it all helps the patient to sleep a little better, to eat more heartily, to recover more quickly.

Laughter does us nothing but good in all sorts of ways and it could be said 'a laugh a day keeps the doctor away.' Oh, I know some will say there's little to laugh about these days. This may be so, but when you get a chance to laugh don't miss it!

4 · YOU AND OTHERS; YOU ALONE

PREGNANCY AND AGORAPHOBIA?

Many women wonder whether or not it is advisable to have a baby whilst they are suffering from agoraphobia. Well, the straight answer is 'Yes, of course.' Why deprive yourself of the joy of having a child just because of some rooted fear that you may pass on your agoraphobia to the child. Ask any agoraphobic woman who, even though she had probably gone through the nine months' waiting period full of doubts as to the wisdom of what she was doing, found once the baby arrived the fears were overshadowed by the elated feeling she experienced on seeing her beautiful son or daughter.

Being a new mother helps to encourage the feeling of wanting to go out and show off the new arrival. It is a wonderful experience to go out of the house, no longer alone, and with a pram or baby carriage to lean on for support. This can also be an opportunity to make new friends among other young mothers who would be met during the baby clinic sessions in your area. What a wonderful chance to invite a new 'mum' back to your home for a cup of tea and a chat. Who knows, she too may be just as lonely as you may have been in the past and would also welcome a new friend.

Agoraphobia as such can never be passed on to a child.

Agoraphobia itself is only a symptom and not a disease or illness or genetic disorder. Remember, however, that anxiety and fear can be communicated.

Having a new life to guide makes one conscious of new responsibilities, which in itself brings more self-confidence and self-esteem: this can only be good for the agoraphobic mother or father.

Rose tells us: My baby girl who was born 10 weeks before her time weighed only 2 lbs 3 oz. She now weighs over 11 lbs. and is doing fine. Her name is Angela and she has helped me tremendously. I find pushing her pram into town and back gives me plenty of confidence. On the way home I still have slight 'panics' but I do get home safely. I have plenty of friends locally and this helps as I can go on short visits. One friend said to me the other day that she had heard it wouldn't be wise to have a baby while still suffering agoraphobia. I told her not to listen — go ahead. It has done me the world of good. It is my fifth child -- unintentional, but loved. I believe she was sent for a reason. At one time I took to drink to enable me to cope with the fear and lack of confidence, but I gave up drinking two years ago. The agoraphobic anxieties, stress, panics etc. all piled up on me about two months after I had stopped drinking. It was like facing reality suddenly: responsibilities came to life after the fog in my mind for nearly ten years. I had a breakdown, but slowly recovered with the help of my husband. I still take tranquillisers but only if I get an attack. The main thing now is that I have the confidence I needed and I don't want to lose all I've gained during these last two years. Perhaps the following slogan is appropriate: *Today is the tomorrow we worried about . . . yesterday.*

Beryl says: I took my baby out for a two mile walk on Saturday, then I went to town in my car with my husband to do some shopping, all without a panic attack. I am going on holiday for the first time in 5 years. My baby helps me such a lot: having her to care for stops me sitting about daydreaming all day and worrying about my agoraphobia.

BEREAVEMENT

This is an experience which we all suffer at some time in life, in childhood, youth, or middle years and, naturally, in old age. To an agoraphobe it is particularly devastating if it means the loss of a beloved and caring husband or wife, especially if one has been a 'leaner' with great dependence on the other. After the funeral is over and the relatives and friends have departed to their own homes, that first night in the house seems to go on forever, although with very many people the reality and finality of the loss does not strike them until some weeks or even months later.

During this interim period it is most unwise of an agoraphobe, or indeed anyone who is bereaved, to leave their home immediately to go to stay with a friend or relative, however well meaning the invitation. The trauma of the eventual return is far greater than 'staying put' either alone or having someone staying with you.

There are so many matters to be dealt with. In the case of a woman, you are now a widow and no longer a wife, which seems very cruel and harsh but is a fact, so insurances, credit cards, memberships, means of income etc. all have to be considered and put in order before one can even take time to mourn.

It is sometimes said that a widow or widower allows herself or himself to go utterly to pieces on the death of the partner. It is understandable when the stark reality has to be faced, and you have every right to do so if you feel the need. Time out has to be taken to mourn, for you to come to terms with your grief. Do not allow anyone, however well intentioned, to tell you that you do not need this breathing space. Take it; you will feel better if you do.

Time does soften the blow, however difficult it is to envisage, time also does away with the 'guilt' feelings that everyone goes through, and all the 'if only's'.

Now comes the hardest part: you have to start living again, by yourself and *for* yourself, combatting that agoraphobia which had probably almost disappeared whilst you were so busy, but has now reared its ugly head again because you feel so depleted and alone. This is the time to make use of any or all of your relatives and friends. *Tell* them of your difficulty and tell them too that you would welcome their company when you wish to go out. Never say 'no' when offered an opportunity to go to the shopping centre, ride in a car, have an afternoon at a neighbour's house having a cup of coffee and a chat. Talk about your partner's death, mention him by name and encourage others to do the same. It acts as a balm to a sorrowing heart and is a tribute to their memory. Invite people back to your home: it all helps to break that barrier of fear which may be lurking around. After all if you cannot deal with all of the outside happenings, at least bring some of the outside world into your own home.

A man is placed somewhat differently insomuch as he usually has his employment to take his mind off his troubles. A surprisingly large number of men do carry on with their jobs even though they suffer agoraphobic difficulties in varying degrees.

Speaking for myself, I am one of those people who pay dearly months after a crisis, so had a great struggle with my own difficulties when widowed. But I did not allow myself to become housebound, and made a determined effort to go out every day, either walking or using public transport, as I felt if I did not do these things I would be letting Eric's memory down and all the care he gave me so many years ago when I was not able to do such things alone. It is *not* easy, and I sympathise greatly with those who are not able to go into a situation which they do not like, especially if, as I am, you are alone. Take heart, and it will come with time. Remember we still have our memories of our partners, even if those memories bring the tears in the dead of night when things seem worse than ever. Another day dawns and who knows, maybe today will start an upward trend towards a lighter heart or maybe a new friend who may turn to us instead for comfort themselves.

I found the following small prayer very helpful at the time of bereavement and indeed still do:

HENGROVE PRAYER
If I can do some good today, if I can serve along life's way,
If I can something helpful say, Lord show me how . . .
If I can do a kindly deed, if I can help someone in need,
If I can sow a fruitful seed, Lord show me how . . .

If I can make a better start, if I can feed a hungry heart,
If I can fill a nobler part, Lord show me how . . .
If I can do some good today, if I can serve along life's way,
If I can something helpful say, Lord show me how.

To many people this article will be of interest. To others who have no knowledge of agoraphobia it will be quite beyond their understanding. This is to give hope to all those who are suffering from this nightmare.

For ten years this wretched thing had affected my life. I could not even open the front door; in fact, I had a divan moved into a lower room as I could not make it up the stairs to the bedroom. My daughter who is now 15 years old had to do everything for me — all those years of her childhood lost forever. I am a widow and my husband died when my little girl was two years old. The start of it all was that after 17 years of perfect marriage my husband died suddenly of a stroke. After that I just went to pieces. I was fortunately able to get a job at the War Office, doing the same work that I did during the war when I was in the A.T.S. Then one morning on my way to work this dreadful panic absolutely engulfed me; my only thought was how to get off the bus. I wanted to jump off but something held me back and I had the presence of mind to just hang on until the next bus stop. I felt quite sure everyone must have thought I had gone completely mad. Anyway I was lucky enough to get a taxi and went straight back to the flat. I never left the house again for years . . . until a day arrived when I was told about a trick many others had used. Take your front door key from your purse and hold it in your hot, sticky hand . . . go to the front door and step outside . . . now, *CLOSE* the door, still holding the key. You now have a choice . . . one, are you going to advance to the gate and start a new life of freedom, or two, are you going to unlock the door and step back inside to the life of a prisoner you have lived for so long? Giving *yourself* this choice many times a day, every day, for say a week will convince you that *nothing* terrible happens and you have your destiny through your own choice to go forward. Take that choice *now*!

ALONE OR LONELY?

If you think about it, there is a difference between the two words 'alone' and 'lonely'. A small number of the population, even some agoraphobes, like to be alone and are quite happy to be so. They have set a pattern to their lives in which they feel self-sufficient and do not wish to change their habits to include anyone else too closely.

However, the vast majority of people, especially agoraphobics, feel lonely a lot of the time. Agoraphobia is said to be one of the loneliest conditions to suffer from, as it starves many from constant contact with people; and the main need of most of us is to communicate through sight, sound and touch, with a mere acquaintance met in the street whilst taking a walk, and in deep and special relationships in which one shares all one's innermost thoughts and feelings.

There are, too, other aspects of loneliness. Do you make your child lonely because you 'have no time to listen', your husband or wife lonely because you are too tired or cannot be bothered to talk or communicate in any way when alone together? After all, one need not necessarily live alone to be lonely. This happens so often even within a family situation or at social gatherings — one can feel totally set apart from others.

Do you turn away from that neighbour or relative who always wants to tell you of her latest problem, in other words to 'cry on your shoulder'? It is only too easy in this instance to think 'Why me?', 'Whose shoulder can I cry on?' That little voice inside you is constantly asking 'Who is going to listen to me?'

Think on this, however: How can you be lonely when there are others who need you? Although it may be a burden to listen and lend an ear to someone else's troubles, it does paradoxically help you insomuch as your self esteem grows through the satisfaction of knowing someone regards you as a friend and feels that you understand and want to help.

What can you do to ease acute loneliness? Drop a line today to someone you have not heard from for a long time; get on the phone to a neighbour asking them to come round for a cup of coffee and a chat. Even housebound agoraphobes can do this as a start to bringing the outside world 'in' . . . until such time as a return visit can be made without difficulty to their place. Always remember someone has to take the first step or utter the first words to begin a conversation which may lead to the start of a new friendship.

I am not suggesting that every agoraphobe should obtain a list of local clubs in an attempt to join this, that or the other, but you might find a small group of people who would be very glad to have a meeting place — why not offer yours? You would not necessarily like everybody, or even what they stand for, but at least it would be an opportunity to find out, wouldn't it?

Learning to cope with loneliness is important in order that self confidence is not lost. Loneliness is no respector of your ego, and it is essential to change the situation before communication is totally lost.

Joy tells us: So much agoraphobia appears to be caused by isolation of one sort or another: the business man taking on more than he can manage (whether admitted or not) and feeling alone; the young housewife with a small child in a strange situation and away from home for the first time, also having to find friends; the older woman or man whose partner never ever seems to communicate with people . . .

I no longer suffer from the agoraphobia which was caused, I know, by a lifetime's isolation of one sort or another. I can now accept the situation through understanding 'why', although it still hurts. The knowledge picked up on the way, and with much reading, was my own work. No authority helped me, no encouragement was given — only the old reply, 'What do you expect me to do?'

The things which have helped me most have been ordinary things: a new bath essence to help me overcome the fear of water; doing my hair in a different way; joining any organisation locally to which I could force myself to attend; talking with people in whatever situation; giving a big warm smile with chin up to whomever needs it. Voluntary work also helps a bit if you are able to do it: although one feels in need of help oneself, it still can be done.

When at the home I knit, I sew, read, but above all I have found it necessary to make light of my 'crying needs'. Acquaintances, even close ones, will shy away, not understanding how little exchange is necessary and afraid of being lumbered . . . even my best friend only sees my smiling exterior. Getting out and about is all up to us. It's hard, I know, but I've done it.

Beryl writes: Trying to combat my loneliness, about two months ago I bought a second-hand bicycle and this has been a wonderful source of 'freedom' for me. Now, however ghastly I feel I can always get out to the local shops or around to see friends who live just a few roads away where, on certain days when I feel very tired, I would not have attempted walking to: I feel a new person when I get home. I had not ridden a bike for 20 years and was not sure I was still going to be able to ride it as I can get quite giddy at times, but I have never had any strange feelings while out riding. I recommend it to any lonely person. In fact, a friend nearby who has agoraphobia also bought a bike recently on the strength of seeing me fly past a few times a day: she is now over the moon with it and says 'it's the answer'.

Agnes says: I have suffered from agoraphobia for three years, and had become very lonely. However, during the last 14 months my lifestyle has changed — I help out at an animal sanctuary. Admittedly it is only five minutes ride away by push bike, but it gets me out of the house twice weekly and to me is a form of relaxation even though I am working. There are all sorts of animals, both household pets and wild animals, so you can imagine there is a lot of feeding, watering and cleaning to do. Money has to be raised to feed all the animals and this is done in many ways which involve meeting people. I can assure you I do enjoy it.

If you can remember always to treat other people as you would wish to be treated, to put yourself in someone else's shoes, you may find your loneliness decreases.

5 · PHYSICAL FITNESS

To answer in a general way the queries from so many people, both male and female, who ask, 'Do other people suffer "physical" illnesses such as gall stones, colitis, spastic colon, diverticulitis, rashes, headaches, a feeling of lethargy and general lack of energy?', the answer is 'Yes, yes, yes — of course, all these things happen to an agoraphobe.' But then what makes everyone think that those things don't happen to people who DO NOT have agoraphobia? One cannot blame agoraphobia for everything, can one? It is very possible that when one is tense, strung up and depressed these 'physical' feelings are much more marked for the simple reason that one is in the house with loads of time on hand to think about them and so make them more noticeable.

HEADACHES AND MIGRAINE

How many housewives have found themselves yelling at the children, 'Stop that noise, you are giving me a headache'; the tired business man after a hard day and a long slow traffic-ridden drive home; a child perhaps revising for exams — all these instances could trigger tension headaches, very often disappearing after a short break and a suitable painkiller such as soluble aspirin.

Naturally, also, there are some headaches which accompany physical illness, and these should be dealt with by whatever medication the doctor has prescribed at the time.

However, there is another rather alarming type of headache called a migraine, which can come on suddenly, in most instances affecting one side of the head only, and accompanied by nausea, perhaps vomiting and a general feeling of malaise. Very often these attacks are preceded by flashing lights and blurred vision . . . the condition in its severest state can be quite disabling, lasting several hours or several days.

All the sufferer wants to do is lie down in a darkened room with absolute quiet. Obviously, most migraine sufferers who have had this condition for many years will have the necessary medication at hand in case of need, although it does not always respond. A first time attack will probably be very frightening — the person may think they are having a 'brainstorm', so it is necessary for a doctor to be summoned to give help and assurance.

Marjorie tells us: I have had migraine since I was a child — I remember my mother putting vinegar soaked rags around my forehead to ease the pain when I was only three years old. Through teenage, marriage, motherhood, widowhood, on and off comes the dreaded lurg. The pains are less these days, but the blank spots of vision, the jazzy lines and sometimes a feeling of disorientation still occur. For myself I find the major cause to be tension, insecurity, depression, although there may be other underlying causes. I have been tested several times for allergies but nothing definite has ever arisen. With many people there are definite allergies — chocolate, cheese, fish, nuts, usually the protein substances; but don't let anything put you off eating these unless it can be proved; it is not necessary to deprive yourself without cause. If you are a sufferer you will already have received doctor's advice on this and you can ask about migraine associations to which you can belong. The UK Association, for example, quotes all sorts of odd tips which people have found helpful, some new drugs and some old wives' tales which do work. There are migraine clinics in many towns and cities and your doctor would give you a letter to take the nearest one should you wish. 'Aggies' who are 'Miggies' as well are almost certain to be in the Anxiety Army, so battle on, release the tension, drop the shoulders down, stop tooth-grinding and have a laugh a day if you can.

Another correspondent says: I can feel real sympathy with migraine sufferers as I too have attacks. I have done so for 41 years of my life and no one has yet been able to offer me any real help. I've turned every stone to try and beat the thing. I am convinced that migraine was the culprit which caused me to become so afraid to go about my life in the usual manner: as the attacks increased my life became narrower.

I run a very organised household and manage my shopping and business by cycling around. If too far I wait for my husband to take me by car. I wonder how many other agoraphobes are the way they are through migraine?

Strange as it may seem, I have gone through various ordeals, plus three operations with flying colours, although no one knew what I was feeling inside!

Remember: The tide also turns at low water as well as at high!

STRESS

It is essential for everyone, including agoraphobics, to have a certain amount of stress in their daily lives. Stress differs from anxiety insomuch as stress gives the motivation to stretch oneself to reach a goal, instead of passively suffering the anxiety and worrying whether such a goal could be achieved. The above is the acceptable stress that should form the basis for self-motivation.

On the other hand, stress can become a burden if it is prolonged, as in the case of a debilitating illness, for example, which could be very wearing, physically, mentally and emotionally, perhaps bringing a tendency to give in to an illness or to retreat. Even agoraphobics can accept the compensation of being ill if they are receiving a great deal of sympathy and attention from family, relatives or visitors. This can become quite a negative way of life. In such circumstances the least discomfort or demanding situation could give rise to a panic attack.

The cause of stress may be emotional, such as worry or anxiety; or biochemical, that is by the release into the body of the substance histamine; or physical, possibly through an illness or injury or even over-exertion.

Everybody is at some time or other exposed to emotional stress in varying degrees and a few people are subject to constant worry and fear but if the stress continues and the person cannot adjust to it then psychosomatic illness may result. The patient may develop headaches; digestive disorders such as intestinal cramp, diarrhoea, peptic ulcer or colitis; asthma, rashes or other allergic symptoms; pain in the chest, circulatory disturbances or rapid heartbeat; and many other symptoms. Treatment includes a thorough evaluation of the patient's situation and the removal of the cause of stress wherever possible.

A psychotherapist says: People with 'physical' difficulties such as upset tummies or constricted throats might find it helpful to remember that human beings tend to react in their bodies in line with what is upsetting them emotionally. A kind of so-called 'organ' language. For example, a constricted throat might well mean there is something in your life you 'cannot swallow'. A bad tummy might mean something you 'cannot stomach' etc. etc.

Arising from this, if you do have some kind of insight about your own behaviour and its causes, remember — insights don't help if you simply use them to dwell on *why* you are like you are. They are only useful if you use them to make the future *different* for yourself.

Therapists always try to remain flexible. They make hypotheses which they test out and then alter as necessary. People attempting to use therapy on themselves should remember that they may often be looking in the wrong direction. If, after a reasonable time of persistence, self-help doesn't seem to be working then be flexible and look into the other areas of your life and emotions.

Remember that stress, even if wholly emotional, naturally gives rise to physical chemical changes in the body. So don't forget to do something physical to use up those chemicals, e.g. flex and unflex your fists quickly for a short period to make your forearm muscles use up the chemicals. In conjunction with calming thoughts it adds one more controlling influence to help you. Calming thoughts may not use up the very real physical chemicals quickly enough!

BEHAVIOUR TYPES A AND B

This person was obviously impatient and tense. One hand was clenching a packet of cigarettes and the other was in a tight fist. He pushed the lift button not once, not twice but six times; then he spotted another lift opposite, muttered a curse, and then dashed out just as the doors closed on the one he had left. Watching him I realised he was displaying what cardiologists call 'Type A' behaviour — hurried, aggressive, impatient and easily angered. Such people are easy targets for a heart attack.

Probably no 'Type A' person would be able or even want to convert completely to a more contemplative, relaxed 'Type B' personality. However, most 'Type A' types would agree that some of their behaviour patterns are as counter-productive as they are personally and socially undesirable. How to make the crucial switch towards 'B'-ness? Here are some tips that should be helpful.

1) Take stock of your life's goals, how you spend your time, what is really important to you and your loved ones. Concentrate on what is worth *being* rather than worth *having*. Stop measuring your life in quantities — number of accomplishments, number of clients, number of committees on which you may serve. Think more in terms of quality. Rid yourself of trivial obligations. You will probably find that doing a few things really well is more enhancing than doing a lot less effectively.

2) Give up trying to be a superperson who, despite a demanding career, insists on retaining control of everything at home, entertaining, participating in community affairs, bringing up perfect children. This can be done only at the expense of your health, your marriage *and* your children. Forget perfection. At home and at work decide what it is that you and you alone must do and then delegate the other responsibilities.

3) Spend some time alone. Attend a concert, visit a museum,

read a thought-provoking book, or just sit quietly and contemplate the sky. Leave yourself more time to get to somewhere or accomplish something. Then if you are delayed you'll be less anxious. Take something to read when you might have to wait around somewhere or practise doing nothing. Study the people around you. Fantasize. Think about someone you love. Think about your life. Have a pleasant conversation with someone.

4) Get up 15 minutes earlier in the morning so that you won't have to start your day in a rush. Your body will appreciate the calm much more than the extra sleep. Stop interrupting others or finishing their sentences. Practise being a good listener, concentrate on what is being said instead of thinking of something that is of greater interest to you, and don't take over from someone doing a job slowly unless he cannot do it at all. Walk away, if you cannot bear to watch. Even when working against a deadline take breaks periodically, stare out of the window, go for a walk, anything to relieve the tension at all times.

5) Don't waste your anger on trivial matters such as a delayed train, an inept waiter or an abrupt shop assistant. In most cases you cannot do anything about it!

6) Avoid contact with people who always raise your hackles. Don't take so seriously those who you must continue to see. Stop focusing on how many people fall short of your ideals. This will only foster disappointment and hostility in others.

7) Make friends with a 'Type B' person. He or she may not say much but will listen well and serve as a model of the relaxed behaviour you seek in yourself.

8) Finally, remember that habitual rushing and excessive competitive behaviour and hostility are the forms of behaviour most closely associated with heart attack. Think about what situations annoy you, and call upon your intellect and sense of humour to get you through!

If you succeed in doing all the above, you will become a paragon of virtue, no one can even compete with!!

NERVOUS DIZZINESS — A PAIN IN THE NECK!

An agoraphobe tells us: I have suffered from dizziness, noises in the head, vision disturbance and severe headaches for years and have trailed from one specialist to another with little relief. As so often happens all my symptoms were eventually written off as 'typically neurotic'. Then we moved to another district and a new doctor. He it was who explained to me that many cases of dizziness are the result of stress and tensions in the neck at the base of the skull. The blood vessels contract and the blood doesn't flow properly around the head, thus upsetting one's balancing mechanism. If you feel your head spinning, find yourself leaning to one side when walking, and feeling generally insecure and muzzy, your natural reaction is to get panicky, build up more tension and cause the whole pattern to repeat itself.

I found it a great comfort to be able to relate my symptoms to a physical happening. I am, with difficulty, teaching myself to relax, especially when I approach one of my panic stations. 'Watch your jaw,' warns my doctor. If your teeth are clenched it's a sure sign that tension is starting to build up. It is a fact that I *don't* get any of these symptoms when I am happy and relaxed.

STRESS INCONTINENCE

Many agoraphobes complain of continually having to 'spend a penny' several times before they go out. Indeed, some will not even leave their homes before ascertaining just where the next toilets are . . . this condition we will call stress incontinence.

The problem of stress incontinence can be helped by training yourself to overcome it. Whatever causes it is not really so important as finding a way to overcome it — always presupposing that the incontinence is not caused by infection which your doctor or clinic will confirm or deny after the necessary tests.

There is a fancy-named muscle called the pubococcygeal muscle which runs from the pubic mound in front to the tailbone at the back and this is the muscle which contains the sphincter muscles which open and close on the body orifices in this area. Ladies can usefully remember the following exercise which, in tensing and relaxing this muscle, will give them greater control over their vaginal muscles and thus will enhance their sexual lives also — a kind of bonus! Recall what it is like to squeeze tight this base muscle, as you imagine yourself sitting on the toilet squeezing back your motions and/or your urine. Practise squeezing the muscle tight, holding it for a few seconds and then releasing. Remember, you can practise this *anywhere*, no one will know what you are doing so occupy any spare moment practising. Next, when you are urinating, practise letting the stream flow then squeezing the muscle and stopping the flow for a second or two then releasing the flow once again. Keep practising this until you have good control.

The third step is to wait until you feel the urge to urinate then deliberately hold it back and go and drink some liquid — water, tea or coffee. After the drink continue to hold back the urine as long as you can. A useful way to help this is to keep reminding yourself that if you can hold it back for one minute you can certainly continue to do it for two minutes, then four minutes is not such a long time further to wait. Keep building up those kinds of thoughts. When you finally have to go off to the toilet — once again let it flow then deliberately stop the flow, release again, and so on. Remember to keep practising tightening and loosening this muscle area for a while every day, anywhere you may be, until you gain good control.

In addition to the fact that you are improving the muscle tone of your sphincters you are also training yourself mentally to realise that you are gaining control, thus improving your confidence in your own abilities.

If you have a good imagination you can usefully add to this some mental imagery. Spend some time of each day resting quietly and bringing into your mind a picture of yourself successfully being in some situation where you control your bladder well. If you decide to do this remember that the strength of the imagery is improved the more of your senses you use. Thus, first create the visual picture then add to it any sounds that might be appropriate then imagine yourself stepping right into that picture and having all the feelings associated with it (for instance, feel your feet on the ground, feel the firm squeezing of your sphincters, sense the temperature of the place where you are in your imagination, etc. etc.). Make quite sure that each image is a successful one and you can even improve this by going back through your past memories until you find one where you fully recall yourself as being full of confidence and managing well. Then when you bring into your mind images of successfully coping with your urine retention you can double expose over the top of it your memory of that successfully confident time from the past. Thus you are actually assisting your body and your mind to work as one unit — successfully — to learn a way to change.

While suffering stress incontinence try going out only for very short walks and try to concentrate on something else — view other people's gardens — anything that will take one's mind off the problem. It is very far from easy but one is very pleased once even a short trip has been successful. Try cutting down on liquid intake for a couple of hours before a trip out. You can always have an extra cup of tea on your return!

DIVERTICULOSIS AND DIVERTICULITIS

If you were told that 80% of our Western population suffer with their 'innards' without even having symptoms, these only coming to light when having an X-Ray/Barium meal for other conditions, you would be surprised wouldn't you?

Diverticulosis is a condition which arises in adults who are victims of chronic constipation or who have had some inflammation of the large bowel. Pockets or diverticula form in the mucous membrane of the bowel and, as faecal matter may collect in them, some inflammation may arise.

Its cause is thought to be the low bulk or lack of fibre in modern civilised man's diet. Primitive man ate large quantities of husks, stalks, rinds and other roughage. A modern diet of refined sugar, white bread and white flour has almost no waste content and as a result the faeces are low in bulk. It is difficult for the muscle of the colon to keep small, hard faeces moving and this causes the colon to thicken. Internal pressure arises and little pouches (called diverticula) of the mucous membrane lining the intestine are forced through the gaps in the muscular outer wall. Spasms in the muscles of the colon cause attacks of gripping pain in the left side of the abdomen and the victim is usually constipated, passing infrequent small, hard stools.

Colonic diverticula show up on X-Ray photographs taken after the patient has had a barium enema. Sometimes diverticula are found during a routine medical check-up without their having caused any trouble but if symptoms are troublesome they usually respond to an increase of bulk in the diet by adding bran or another bulk laxative twice a day. One man described to me his doctor's verdict on his X-Ray — 'You have got bubbles in your guts, old boy' and promptly put him on a diet of fruit and vegetarian dishes for a while. This soon cleared the discomfort, and surgery indeed is very seldom needed in mild cases.

Therefore, as an aid to overcoming this condition one has to change one's food from the soft and soggy to those containing fibre as a means of creating bulk in the colon — in other words give your innards something to work on. Food such as unrefined cereals, wholemeal bread, bran cereals, beans and baked beans, peas, sweetcorn and baked potatoes (including the skin) are all wonderful.

Those who have had the unpleasant symptoms of constipation, slight blood losses and aches and pains around the groin area can rest assured that altering the diet to include these fibrous foods will, after about a month or possibly six weeks, improve matters markedly. More relaxation and less anxiety and obsession about the innards will also help to improve things. Try also to take more exercise, preferably in the open air to help your system get going!

COLITIS

Doctors admit that no one can yet say which comes first — whether stress causes colitis or whether it is the other way round. Whichever the case, it is an extremely uncomfortable condition in which diarrhoea is very much present, sometimes being chronic, especially in the nervous, anxious, obsessional type of person. It is sometimes known as spastic colon. Paradoxically, faeces are sometimes very difficult to pass (this is when many folk turn to taking laxatives continually, thus making another vicious circle as a bowel which has to depend on this kind of thing becomes too lazy to use its own muscles to do the work they are meant to do).

A person having established colitis can feel very irritable, depressed, with a feeling of low spirits and lack of enthusiasm.

One of the first things to do about the condition of colitis is to eliminate any cause of infection, such as bad teeth, infected tonsils etc. as these can have an effect on your innards. Try to cultivate an optimistic outlook on life in general so that your guts can settle! Do not be afraid of eating for goodness sake, as there is nothing worse for your poor inside than to be empty and the muscles having nothing to work on.

INSOMNIA

Of the many forms of mental suffering it is doubtful if there is any to be compared with the affliction of persistent sleepless nights. We all know that the occasional wakeful night does occur without causing much disruption the following day other than a slight feeling of lassitude. However, the person who becomes a habitual insomniac eventually feels quite ill as his body steadily declines in general health and vitality, causing irritability, loss of appetite, physical weakness and a blunting of one's mental efficiency towards any tasks, with a certainty of making agoraphobia a bigger problem than ever to be faced.

Without going into the medical aspect of how or why we sleep, we know that everyone needs those hours of blankness and relaxation, during which the body recharges itself and the brain and mental processes are, or should be, at rest.

There are many reasons why wakefulness can occur: pain through aching limbs, indigestion through unwise meals shortly before retiring, worry and tension through taking problems to bed with you, for example, but the main thing is not to be over-anxious about the number of hours you think you ought to sleep. Many of us can manage with far less than we believe to be the norm.

Let us now think of practicalities which may help to bring about more restful nights. Is the bedroom to your liking colourwise? Is it too hot/too cold? Is the bed mattress too hard/too soft? Are the bedclothes too heavy/too light? Are you using too many pillows? All these things seem trivial perhaps but merit some consideration for essential comfort.

Correct preparation leading towards bedtime can also help a great deal. At least an hour beforehand teach yourself to 'wind down'; refrain from eating a heavy meal too late, thus preventing an overful stomach; perhaps take a short walk to ease up the tension in your muscles; take a leisurely warm (not hot) bath; indeed pamper yourself and sit brushing your hair for a few minutes afterwards (this action is very soothing and beneficial to the hair anyway). When you feel yourself ready, prepare a warm milky drink and take it to bed with you, sipping this and maybe reading a light book is all conducive to making you feel more relaxed which in turn helps sleep to come.

On no account get into that bed with a fixed determination that you are going to sleep, come what may — that will surely kill any attempt at relaxation and a sleepless night will result.

Should all these self-help ideas fail to bring you the relief you crave then by all means have a talk with your doctor, who can prescribe tablets to be taken before you retire, to help break the habit of wakeful nights. Be warned, however, that these drugs do not induce a natural kind of sleep and very often give you a 'hangover' effect the following morning. It is wiser to try managing without them, and certainly if you do resort to taking tablets only use them for a short period of time.

Stella tells us: My solution to wakeful nights, which had dogged me for over three months, was to get up! I turned my life upside down, as it were, by pretending I was a night worker. Not the practical solution for everyone of course, but as I lived alone it did not interfere with anybody.

All my housework, including washing and ironing, and my hobbies were all dealt with during the night hours. I went to bed at 7.30 a.m. and found I could rest comfortably and sleep until about 5.30 in the afternoon.

Over a period of about six months I gradually went to bed later in the morning and slept later into the evening until I was eventually going to bed at a normal time at night, rising in the morning at my 'old' time.

I also taught myself relaxation during this period, which no doubt helped me enormously, so I face nights now without wakefulness.

Joan tells us: Please don't lose faith in everything and everyone. Faith is your most precious thing to help you get through the bad times, especially faith in God. Pray each day. Don't stop trying, you may be getting older but you are never 'too old'. Age does not matter — you are just as good as anyone younger. I had insomnia for several years and I hope these few tips which helped me may help others: 1) If you cannot sleep do not worry about it — put on the light and read. 2) Make sure you are not hungry — eat something before bed, take a teaspoon of natural honey (keep by your bed in case you wake). 3) Calcium helps to relax you. Take 4-6 Bone Meal tablets before bed, (available from any health store). 4) When you lie in bed check you are not tense. Go limp, do not clench your teeth, try to feel like floating. Think of nice things, count your blessings and pray.

I offer no apologies for including a light-hearted piece which was sent to me some years ago by someone who suffered from this serious problem but who managed to see the funny side of it.

Confessions of an insomniac

There was a time when I could take my 'ravelled sleeve of care' to bed with me and wake up the next morning with every strand of it 'knit up' into a cardigan perfect from cuffs to collar. Alas, no more. I've become the genuine, hard-core insomniac to whom R.E.M. stands not for the Rapid Eye Movement of dreams but rather for wakefulness, the Rankest Enemy of Man.

As my mirror attests, you can spot the true insomniac at a glance: those black circles round his eyes that suggest a stunted racoon; that sagging of the lower lip so reminiscent of an old dray horse on its way to the glue factory. Catch his expression — that of a rotting snowdrift . . . and if you could get inside his head, his thoughts would look like something drizzled on . . . See how the bed is caused to look inviting, soothing . . . and at first it is. You lie there curled up in the shape of a shrimp or a cashew nut, blissfully comfortable . . . until IT springs its trap . . . Suddenly something begins to insist that it's the other pillow your head would rest easier on. You shift position, only to find the second pillow is no more hospitable than the first . . . then panic strikes! Your mind begins to chase itself like a dog chasing its own tail (at least mine does) in a jumble of thoughts that leap hard on each other's heels without rhyme or reason. A sample goes like this:

First, the apprehensions, *did* I pull out the plug on the T.V.? Do I smell smoke? Should I make a Will? Next, attempting to distract my brain I set myself the most outlandish questions. Can I list the Seven Deadly Sins? I get all but one. What are the Seven Wonders of the World? Who first took a look at a sheep and grasped the principle of knitting? Would it help if I ate something? I go to the kitchen and made a sandwich . . . Ah, that is the Sin I was looking for — Gluttony!!

Back in bed, succumb to hypochondria. What if that burst of wind signals diverticulosis? ONE O'CLOCK . . . Should I take a sleeping pill? No, pills are useless and to borrow some words from Othello, not 'poppy, not mandragora, nor all the drowsy syrups of the world' are worth a damn. ONE-THIRTY . . . My God, has it only been half an hour since I looked at my watch? TWO O'CLOCK . . . There's not a book of any interest in the house. I start to read Bartlett's *Familiar Quotations* — it's like eating an endless meal of chicken-liver pâté. FOUR O'CLOCK . . . I try to keep my groans as inaudible as possible. I wouldn't want to disturb Rip Van Winkle. For a few minutes I doze fitfully, dream a garbled dream, wake up again, crying aloud Hamlet's anguished plaint 'Now I am alone'.

I wonder if there is an all-night chemist open: I suppose it would do no harm to *try* that mandragora. Which syllable does the accent fall on in the word 'mandragora'?

Miraculously, and before I know it, I drowse again — this time, pleasantly. I begin to dream of green pastures and clouds of fleecy wool . . . at which moment the alarm clock rings! I leap from the bed like a trout — and sigh like a winded pack-horse with each trouser leg I draw on.

Good morning all you lucky people who don't know that grisly ogre, insomnia. Would you please wipe that smug, totally rested look off your faces??

Barbara writes: One's brain doesn't feel half so tired after a couple of weeks of good, restful nights, especially if you go to bed after getting yourself ready in a leisurely fashion — perhaps having a slow wash or shower, brushing your hair for ten minutes, floating around in your dressing gown making yourself a nice warm drink, perhaps taking it upstairs to bed with you. The secret is to do things slowly and not rush madly round making yourself worked up before you get to bed. Then make yourself comfortable, sip your drink and put on your radio and listen to some quiet music.

FATIGUE

Tired? Of course you are from time to time. There is the pleasant, happy feeling after a job well done or a match well played, when you look forward to a nice hot bath in which you will relax, knowing the aches and pains in your body will magically disappear, leaving you with a feeling of well-being and 'all's well with your world'.

This is one side of 'tiredness' we have all happily experienced at one time or another, but what of the insidious, gradually-creeping-on sort of tiredness — a genuine fatigue of the body and spirit we really do not notice over a long period until one day, 'Wham', we wake up feeling as if we have come to the end of the line. The body protests and aches intolerably when we arise from bed and mentally one wonders how to get through the oncoming day.

Perhaps you have had several months of stress and tension, due to influences of family illness, low finances or just struggling with your own efforts to overcome agoraphobia. There is nothing more fatiguing than one's own mental state when under pressure to 'do the right thing' and yet feeling somewhat of a failure.

Nervously ill people suffering from mental fatigue feel that the struggle is becoming too much to bear, their lack of concentration on any idea other than the way they feel, the feeling of unreality which does rear its head at this time makes the sufferer more confused than ever and never at peace within themselves.

Body muscles become continually tense thus causing the familiar aches and pains, adding more misery, the sufferer feeling as if he is too ill to move about. There is usually a certain amount of depression found to be accompanying this type of mental or emotional fatigue, as one gets to feel as if one will never be well or energetic again. Rest assured: it does pass if tackled with patience without guilt.

Firstly, accept that you are like this and will be for quite a while, no matter what anyone says. You have to proceed in your own time and at your own pace, even if you have to reorganise some facets of your lifestyle. If you have employment, do try to delegate some of your workload if possible but carry out the rest to the best of your ability — do try to stay in your job as long as you can, as staying at home doing nothing at all will only give you longer days to dwell on your problem.

If a housewife or a woman at home alone, do set aside certain times of the day for yourself, time to read (trash if necessary, it does not need a great deal of concentration!), time to sew (if you can thread a needle you can make a dress), time to 'beautify' yourself (it will boost your morale somewhat perhaps to change the colour of your hair!). These are all essential times to recharge your batteries, and are not detrimental to your families. Don't feel guilty about your 'time out'. It will not hurt anyone to come to a house where the furniture does not sparkle quite so brightly because you are too tired to polish it every day. Your family won't starve if you positively hate cooking at this time — use convenience foods if you can get them, or ask family to help or bring something in that you can share also.

Try to rally family members and friends around at this time to give all the help they can — even small children can be taught to make their own beds each morning and will have a sense of importance trailing around after Mum with a duster in their hand 'helping' her.

No family? Well, this is more difficult naturally, but do try to cosset yourself just the same, giving yourself time to rest. *Enjoy* the rest; don't feel guilty about it. There will come a day, for you too, when a spark of interest in something will tempt you to try a new project, however haltingly at first, until the day will dawn when you find you are literally rushing through your chores to *make* more time to carry out your new interest!

It is so very true that when one is doing a job or a new hobby which holds the interest, fatigue goes out of the window. The tension aches and pains will vanish and you become your old self once again. Interest is tension's worst enemy.

None of this is achieved overnight and it does take time, but accept this as a fact and do not consider it a waste: it is all part of living and if you now welcome each day as it comes, living one day at a time as you taught yourself to do whilst so fatigued, your family, friends and neighbours will see the new 'you' as you see yourself.

The lessons learned during this fatigued period should help you to prevent getting into such a state again. You probably will have some patches when the old signs return, but if you have taught your mind not to expect too much either from yourself or others around you, you will not allow them to defeat you again.

Florence writes: I have found since and through my bad times renewed hope and courage which I never thought possible. It has been discovered I have a kidney condition after years of faints and becoming phobic. I still do not know which came first, I only know that when I was told it was 'nerves' I pushed myself too hard and became absolutely exhausted. I have always tried to help everyone I could — willingly and cheerfully — and do not regret this. I long to be able to do all that and more again. I know I am not too well at present but have brightness in myself and that combats the bad times. I feel the fears come over me but I also have the peace and secure feelings I've always longed for within myself. It would be beautiful not to have those fears but they do come. People around me grumble about the wet, dreary days; I find I'm thankful to feel the rain on me: I never mind getting wet — it is so refreshing. To fail is not to be a failure — this is a good motto.

HYPERVENTILATION

We should all be aware of a breathing problem called 'hyperventilation'. Basically all it means is *over*breathing, or breathing too fast. Many people who suffer from nervous tension or agoraphobia suffer from overbreathing without knowing it. They overbreathe unconsciously by taking rapid, shallow breaths and this increases their tension and anxiety. They sigh or yawn often and complain, 'I can't seem to take a deep breath and feel short of air.' In fact their problem is not that at all.

What hyperventilation does is create an imbalance of oxygen and carbon dioxide in the blood. Too much and too rapid breathing forces out an unnatural amount of carbon dioxide. As a result the carbon dioxide in the lungs and in the blood becomes abnormally low. This produces a lessened blood and oxygen supply to the brain and the rest of the organs. Then comes such symptoms as faintness, rapid pulse, perspiration, numbness in hands and feet and extreme anxiety. Breathing into a paper bag for a few minutes can make these symptoms disappear by rebuilding the carbon dioxide balance.

Many anxious patients have been helped by learning how to breathe correctly. Anxiety and breathing are so tied together that in helping the one it improves the other. Some people have given up tranquillisers, sleeping pills and other sedatives when they learned to breathe correctly. Every chronically nervous person should check with his doctor to make certain that hyperventilation is not complicating the picture. He could save himself years of unnecessary suffering. Most anxiety sufferers who overbreathe don't realise that it is one of the causes of their discomfort.

Picture a woman sitting tensely in her doctor's surgery as she relates her complaints. She holds her hands firmly on the sides of her chair until her knuckles are white: 'Will I ever get over being scared? I'm afraid to go to work, afraid to go shopping, afraid to sit through an entire film . . . I get the urge to run out because everything is closing in on me . . . I wonder why I should get out of bed in the morning. Every day I have to fight to face the world. I feel this hopelessness will never end.' The doctor watched this young woman as she spoke, noticed that she sighed a lot and quite often put up her hand to cover a yawn. You could see her chest going up and down rapidly. Unquestionably she was overbreathing. After a complete examination the doctor found no evidence of organic disease. He told her let's conduct an experiment. I want you to breathe as deeply and as fast as you can — at least thirty times a minute — for one or two minutes. She sat there breathing fast and deep. Within a minute her face became taut, she clutched her chest and looked up with frightened eyes. 'I'm having an attack. The same as I always get when I'm scared to death. My feet and hands are numb and my heart is racing.' The doctor gave her a brown paper bag to rebreathe in and within a minute or two her symptoms had disappeared. 'There's the proof,' he said. 'One of your problems is unconscious overbreathing. Until you become aware of your breathing you will continue to have these bad, frightening spells.' Within weeks this patient was having fewer attacks of hyperventilation because she would catch herself in time to prevent these episodes of rapid breathing. Although this woman did not miraculously lose all her nervous attitudes and discomforts she announced the last time I met her that she was very much improved.

Overbreathing may be only one of the side-effects of anxiety itself, but, like the chicken and the egg problem of deciding which came first, it is often difficult to know whether anxiety produces the rapid breathing or whether hyperventilation is the instigator of the anxiety. Whichever comes first any patient suffering from anxiety would undoubtedly be helped if we could teach him how to breathe, and thus remove such frightening symptoms as trembling numb hands and feet, heart palpitation, and actual panic. Those who suffer from 'anxiety state' have a feeling that it will never end, their fears often known only to themselves and their doctors. The doctor above was delighted when that same woman came into his surgery about a year later for a short check up. 'I'm really only here for a social call,' she said. 'Just to let you see how an anxious person can become normal again. You know how close I was to a complete nervous breakdown only a year or so ago. I was severely depressed and thought I would never get better. Since I have stopped overbreathing I have been able to face fears one at a time and not let them overcome me.'

BREATHING FOR RELAXATION

For free, one can learn or at least teach and train oneself to breathe properly. At this moment are you breathing shallow, small breaths? Or fairly fast breaths which bring on those palpitations? Just stop now and think about it. Now think about how large an area your lungs cover inside your rib-cage — think about the very bottom area of *your* lungs. Have they had any oxygen lately? Start *today*!

First thing in the morning take at least 5 really deep breaths — in slowly — hold for say 1, 2, 3 then exhale equally slowly. You may find this difficult at first and it may make you a little lightheaded. If so, take only 3 deep breaths as a start and then gradually work up to as many as you can. The main thing is to do the whole exercise SLOWLY to get the full benefit. Eventually you will find during the day a minute or two of this deliberately deep breathing will bring a feeling of relaxation.

Another type of breathing is used by chest sufferers and sportsmen. This is diaphragmatic breathing, when you use, as the name implies, your diaphragm (that's the part between your rib-cage in the front just above your 'stomach area'). Place your hand literally just on your waist frontwise and take a deep breath so that this area will then be pressing against your hand. When you exhale your hand should go back almost to your backbone!

Remember all those 'fluttery' feelings you get in your stomach when tensed up? Five minutes of this type of breathing will steady them down and also make you feel much more relaxed. You really must take deep breaths with this one, so inhalation really does give the impression that your 'middle' swells and exhalation must be equally thorough as before. Just do it a couple of times to begin with, working up gradually until you automatically do this even when outside and feel a bit panicky. No one else will know that you are carrying with you your own relaxation therapy.

Just a reminder: your mouth is for talking, eating and drinking, not for breathing. Use the old *nose* — it was meant for air intake!

HYPOCHONDRIA CAN DAMAGE YOUR HEALTH!

Having looked at the very real physical damage which can occur let us ponder a moment on hypochondria. There is only one prescription for this invisible, hightly contagious disease: patient, heal thyself!

No form of ignorance is so widespread as ignorance about pain: what it is, what actually causes it, and how to cope with it without panic. Almost everyone can list the names of at least a dozen drugs that can be used to deaden pain for every conceivable cause, from headache to haemorrhoids. Far less known is the fact that a great many pain symptoms are self-limiting, that they are not always a sign of poor health, that they are frequently the result of tension or insufficient sleep, overeating, smoking, excessive drinking, inadequate exercise, stale air or even boredom. The surest way of eliminating pain is to eliminate the abuse. Pain increases with fear. The fear that the pain may be an indication of grave illness can in itself create other symptoms lacking organic significance. Doctors' surgeries are overloaded with people who are terrified because of minor pains and are convinced that something dreadful is happening to them.

Instead of being able to give adequate attention to patients genuinely in need of treatment, doctors now find their time soaked up by people who have nothing wrong with them except a temporary indisposition. Many patients feel indignant if the doctor tells them that their pain is nothing serious. In fact, most feel they really haven't got their money's worth from a visit to the doctor unless they are told that they need medication. But if ignorance about the nature of pain is widespread ignorance about painkilling drugs is even more so. What is not generally understood is that many painkillers alleviate pain without correcting the underlying condition. Thus the star sportsman with a torn muscle or tissue damage may need sustained rest more than anything else . . . but his team is battling to win, so the trainers reach into their kitbags for a strong dose of painkiller . . . Presto, the pain disappears! . . . The star performs superbly, but it could be his last good game because the drug didn't repair the muscle or cause the tissue to heal. What did it do? It relieved the symptoms, enabling him to play hard . . . further damaging himself.

The most popular of all painkillers, of course, is aspirin (and compounds containing aspirin) — and deservedly so. These drugs are generally considered to be some of the safest available. Painkilling drugs are one of the great advances in medical history. Properly used they can be a boon in alleviating suffering and in treating disease. However, their indiscriminate use is making psychological cripples and chronic ailers out of millions of people. Perhaps the time has come to make knowledge about pain an important part of our children's school curriculum. For the population at large perhaps some of the same techniques used to make people cancer-conscious can be used to counteract the growing terror of pain and illness. People ought to know that nothing is more remarkable about the human body than its recuperative drive, given the respect it deserves.

PRACTISE TRANQUILLITY

Underlying all that has been said we can discern the message to train ourselves to be comparatively unaffected by the ups and downs, pin-pricks and irritations, injustices and insults which at some time or other affect us all. Our task is not simply to meet individual and isolated situations with an anti-resentment technique but to develop the permanent quality of peace which buffers us against life's assaults. The practice of physical and mental relaxation exercises; the tranquillity to be developed by reading poetry or listening to music as a mental therapy; the practice of prayer and meditation — these are some of the ways in which we can build up the ability to deal with resentment when it arises and even to prevent much of it ever happening.

Learn to believe in yourself. Think constantly of your success, not your failures. Think of the success of others and build up your confidence that what you have to attempt will be successfully accomplished. Affirm constantly, 'I can — and I will.' If you will simply direct your attention towards the tranquil state you will experience the tranquil state. You will become that which you contemplate becoming.

6 · HOW TO COPE

This chapter contains letters from past sufferers. They give advice and explain that recovery is not always plain sailing.

SETBACKS DURING RECOVERY

Many people over the years who have recovered from their agoraphobia find they experience a recurrence of the problem — in short, they have a setback.

Children see any setback as a catastrophe because they think in literal, all-or-nothing terms. Only through experience of living do they learn to accept that not every day will be the same, that there are 'good' days and 'bad' days and that each day is a new experience with many different pressures and different outside influences.

Agoraphobes tend to retain some of this literal, all-or-nothing thinking, which makes a setback such a devastating event. A 'bad' day is not an acceptable concept to the agoraphobe because he does not think of it in terms of *one* day — he thinks of it in terms of forever. When the setback comes, it is as if every success was just a fluke. He becomes aware only of his feelings, feels lost and out of control and this can reinforce anxiety to the point that it escalates into panic. The person may then revert to the old pattern of avoidance. At this point he might even consider that he is back where he started, but more likely — because he has tasted success and because he has a tendency to exaggerate — he feels he has become much worse.

Many agoraphobics have so much difficulty identifying their feelings that they get lumped into one awareness: 'anxiety' or 'upset' or 'panic'. Excitement, pleasure, grief, loneliness, anger and disappointment are not identified and as a result the agoraphobic has great difficulty during a setback relating what he is feeling with regard to what is going on in his life and the world around. In fact, he is turning inward at this point, and this will only add anxiety to whatever feelings are being experienced. It is at this point that he needs to stop, look, listen and then take stock of what is happening in his life.

One can get out of a setback if one proceeds in a systematic manner. The first thing the agoraphobe in a setback needs to do is quietly *accept* the fact that something is occurring, or has occurred, that they are reacting to in a negative way.

Once the agoraphobe has identified the problems he then needs to set a priority as to which ones are affecting him the most and require to be solved first. Then a plan of action must be set and followed through in order to solve the problem and obtain satisfaction.

Getting out of a setback is a step-by-step process, not an immediate achievement. It defies the old habit patterns of avoidance because it is an active process. One needs to remember that in order for the agoraphobe to be in a setback he must have made some progress before. He had to have learned the skills and achieved some successes in order to experience the setback in the first place . . . so soldier on with hope.

Joan writes: I often liken myself to a train journey. Sometimes one travels along in sun and daylight, comparatively speedily, with occasional hang-ups and troubles, but at least getting along — things to see and do. Then one is plunged unexpectedly into a tunnel, sometimes long, sometimes short — perhaps occasional glimpses of daylight coming from above with a light, however small, in the far distance. Sometimes the train stops in the tunnel for what seems an eternity, nothing can move and one is left alone in the dark. Friendly voices may be heard attempting to get through but they seem far off. Then, perhaps for no apparent reason, the train begins to lurch forward again, slowly at first then beginning to reach again for the sunlight, and one hopes to surge ahead once again. Perhaps, with acceptance, one can become the driver of the train and not just a helpless passenger. In the meantime one just hopes that drugs etc. are the oilcan to make the signals move once more.

I thought I would try Origami or paper folding as a new interest. I know the thought of just fiddling around with bits of paper might seem time-wasting, and there are times when one just screws the whole thing up and throws it into a corner. Although very much a beginner I manage to make some good things. I still remember the look of amazement on a little girl's face when I presented her with a swan made from the silver paper from a cigarette packet (we happened to be on a train journey at the time!). If one doesn't mind some odd looks, it can distract one if in a panic whilst travelling. I seem to have got back to the railway once again!!

Sue writes: I would like to mention the guilt feelings I have at having to give up work and also give up going shopping alone etc., due to agoraphobia. In fact I suffer guilt feelings whenever, through setbacks, I am prevented from leading a normal life. We are told to do a little more each day, go forward and set targets, but in many cases this does not appear to work. I have tried very hard, never giving in, feeling angry when exhausted, trembling over nothing at all. I feel for some agoraphobes it is better to do exactly the opposite. For those who seem to be getting nowhere, if you can let it all wash over you, do as little as possible until the time is right. Accept help while you recover quietly. I do not mean to be selfish and 'enjoy' it but going along at your own pace may help your own particular case.

Mrs H. writes: I cannot understand how some people can say they would rather stay at home in case a panic comes over them. Surely to *expect* a panic is almost admitting defeat? I find that a panic can strike anywhere, very often at home where is it more difficult to shake off. If we are alone we have more time to dwell on our state of mind, hence the onset of an

95

almost permanent state of anxiety culminating in panic attacks. I realise people who are really terrified of going outside feel safer at home but many of us can go out if accompanied, especially by car. If we are going to panic, why not outside? At least we will have benefited from the fact we have been out! Usually the panic will come, but, more important, it *will* go!

I had a very bad panic attack when in town last week — we were stuck in a traffic jam. I had all the usual symptoms and although was paralysed with fear I had a strong urge to leap out of the car and run but, of course, I didn't. The panic soon subsided and because there was so much to see the incident was soon forgotten. Had I been at home I would probably have dwelled on the incident and more than likely brought on another attack.

This brings me to a few helpful tips on coping with a panic in the car. Firstly, always fasten your seatbelt. Apart from the obvious safety reason it gives one a sense of security. If you have a car radio tune it in to keep your mind occupied — as loud as you dare. Suck a strong mint and wear dark glasses. Keep the sun visor down. Try and stick to the quieter streets and roads. If you have to go into a busy town note all the side roads. These are 'escape routes' and as long as you know they are there you'll usually be all right. Also, when in town try to park as near to the shops as possible and avoid peak times. If possible avoid motorways and stick to quieter routes where you can stop and take a break if you want to.

If the worst does happen and a panic strikes, tighten your seatbelt so that it is firm across your tummy, sit bolt upright and breathe deeply. Literally ride the panic out! Also concentrate your attention on one thing, e.g. the contents of handbag, go through it methodically and slowly until the panic has subsided. Then slowly divert your attention to whatever may be going on around you. Breathe deeply all the time. If you frantically try to divert your attention to the panic it is heightened and prolonged.

SOME PROVEN HINTS AND TIPS

Do not accept defeat. Remember, it is never too late to give yourself another chance, to try another approach.

Do not run away from fear by avoidance. Put the fear into perspective (measure it with reality) . . . it is no more than a physical feeling and will not destroy you.

Recognise that the strange physical sensations connected with your problem are temporary, accept them and recall the fact that you have had them before and they do go away.

Be occupied calmly, not feverishly, in trying to forget yourself or rid yourself of the uncomfortable, uneasy sensations. Practise relaxation.

Accept the fact that you are human and cannot be perfect. Habits are learned over a period of time and it takes time to correct and replace them with constructive habits of thoughts and feelings.

Feelings are subjective: be aware of them, accept them, but don't let them hold you back. Avoidance is your jailer.

Do not compare yourself with others. Comparison with others leads to negative thoughts and feelings, part of the destructive habit pattern you have developed.

Practise *non-avoidance*. Get involved in the present and this will alleviate the preoccupation with negatives in the past and negative 'what ifs' about the future.

Learn new approaches and methods of handling fear and anxiety. It is not easy, it takes courage and repetition, but practice makes possible what in the beginning seemed improbable.

When you learn to live more in the present and less in the future your body will be subject to less stress, and your mind — of which it is an inescapable part — will share in the feelings of relaxation and well-being. Swim with the stream of life, not against it. Cultivate the art of just letting things happen. The greatest asset in life is the ability to live with it.

The big build-up, the chronic 'always with you' panic feeling, is everybody's bugbear. Apprehension before an event is almost always the worst part. Never plan too far in advance if possible. Make a sudden decision to buy that loaf of bread, post that letter, make that overdue agonising journey to the street corner — alone, and in daylight! Tell yourself you will turn back when you have counted up to ten, then count to ten again.

Wheels are a great help. Agoraphobics are known to have a new baby just so that they have something to push along the road. Scooters and mopeds are very helpful, as are bicycles; even if you cannot ride a bike you can push it along and lean on it when necessary. Then there is always the good old shopping trolley to pull along . . . (useful for carrying the shopping too!).

Lids of all sorts are useful. 'How I wish I was a snail or a tortoise and could carry my house with me!' That is what so many sufferers of agoraphobia often say. It is a well-known fact that many housebound agoraphobics can venture out of their homes at night. Does a dark sky give the comfort of a roof? Rainy days are welcomed as one can carry an umbrella. Most agoraphobics dread a clear blue sky and hot sunshine. Wear a large brimmed hat. Dark glasses are a great comfort; one has the sense of being able to hide behind them.

Plan distractions for when you are out. Think about making yourself talk to strangers; look straight ahead. Don't look up at all costs; concentrate on the contents of shop windows as you pass. Be sure you have a supply of strong peppermints or chewing gum with you. Some people prefer glucose tablets. It helps if you whistle, hum or carry the smallest transistor radio you can buy. Never be without a newspaper or magazine to glance at when under stress. Wear low heeled shoes and walk on grass when possible. A dog is a helpful companion but be careful when choosing one as a highly strung type is likely to pick up your agoraphobic tendencies — then you are in trouble!

Do something creative or constructive. Painting by numbers sets are marvellous for would-be artists. Even if you are physically housebound there is no need to let your mind stagnate. Be adventurous with your reading; get away from fiction and choose a variety of books (or get someone else to) from your library. Paint a picture, write a poem, decorate a room, learn to type. If you can read a recipe you can cook. Cultivate an enthusiasm for something — *anything*.

Michael tells us: I used to be very pessimistic about a cure but a strange thing happened today and now I am optimistic. I was with a friend in a panicky situation and would have left had he not *talked* me through it. I have the feeling the way ahead is now open although there may be many more difficult situations I will have to cope with before I can claim I am back to normal. I used to be very unhappy when I read of encouragement to sufferers such as 'never give up', 'keep on trying' because I felt it was impossible for me to follow other people's advice and get any results. In fact, I did give up for many years and thought I was saddled with my fears for life. So take heart those of you who at present feel life is impossible. I did once. A solution may be round the corner.

A vicar's wife writes: My husband has had to travel long distances away from me and although I am agoraphobic I am quite calm both before he goes and while he is away. At last I am finding religion and prayer helpful. I have prayed that God should increase my faith, deepen my trust and give me His peace . . . and it's working. So I would say to anyone who is not finding their religion helpful 'do not despair, go on practising.' Life for me is full just now. I work mornings at the out-patients department of my local hospital and find this does help my mind to be happily occupied. I have my home and family to see to, also a dog and I take her to obedience classes and for walks. I have had to do some sorting out of priorities so that I can get enough rest. I do feel many agoraphobics are highly talented, capable people who tend to take on too much.

John says: I took courage in both hands and joined a local amateur archaeology group. I did back out of two meetings before I finally made it and felt very bad about that. Once I got there it was fine. We do field surveys and I do a bit of walking so bought a walking stick to get me up the cliffs, and to lean on when stationary. It is a very useful 'prop' but I do find in any case that once I am out on a survey trip I forget my agoraphobia.

P. Pellow, a psychotherapist, says: The first thing to remember is that I am not uncaring — whatever my words may seem like in print. I know myself what it is like to walk the streets ready to burst into tears without provocation, and to feel so desperately lonely that crowds of people cannot help you, and even the one who loves you cannot reach into your loneliness.

Secondly, whatever we do we are only finding ways to give ourselves an edge to beat our sickness (or fears or whatever). In this game anything is fair, any trick or deception. Remember, for instance, how women give themselves a boost by having a new hair-do or buying a new dress and use this idea in an extended way. You can start to change your whole viewpoint by commencing on small things first, the things easiest to change. For example, alter your hairstyle a little, change your style of dress — if you wear jeans and blouses, change to dresses or suits; tie your shoe laces in a different way (turn the laces to make the bow in a different direction); if you go to the pub stand in a different spot from the one where you normally stood before; when you walk to a beauty spot — if you always view it from one place then stand in a different place, some yards away from the usual one. Walk on the opposite site of the road to the one you always used before, or walk a different way round. If you think these things are silly, try them and you will find they are not so silly after all.

Thirdly, tackle things gradually. This teaches you how to accept small amounts of fear at a time, and thus you learn to cope with small amounts first, giving you the strength to go on to the next step and so on. If you try to plunge into a bad fear situation, unless you know what you are doing (and this takes a skilled therapist) you are actually teaching yourself to have fear, not to get rid of it. Split your fear situation down into small steps and tackle each step gradually until you can cope well enough to go on to the next step with more confidence.

Fourthly, you may find you have a need to worry about something. Only a good therapist (and I stress good) can help you rid yourself of such a need, but you can do a lot for yourself by looking into yourself to see if you can find a lesser fear to fasten your worries on, a fear that you can cope with more easily. Doing this may well distract you enough from the original fear to allow you to cope with it better. That is to say, use a lesser fear to distract your mind from the worse fear.

Fifthly, never forget that all family members interact with each other and they all have things to gain or lose from the illnesses of other family members. Do not waste time allocating blames or faults, it won't get you anywhere. Instead look for those things from the other family members that place you in a position which coerces you to stay ill, and try to find ways of coping with them that help the other family members to change attitudes. Do it all gently without blame or criticism: treat it as a fact of life to be looked at soberly and sensibly.

C.B. writes: Until recently I was too scared to admit to anyone I was agoraphobic but over the past months I have gradually opened up to family and friends and have indeed been pleasantly surprised at their help and understanding. Also an understanding psychiatric nurse has taught me how to relax. I now don't panic so easily while I am at home alone (something that used to frighten me very much). This time last year when only going to the local shops with friends was sheer hell — sometimes I would run back home in a blind terror. However, I can now go into the main shopping centre by bus, knowing that if I do panic it will not last for ever and I will not drop dead. Most of all I now have the power to control IT, whereas once IT controlled me!

Margaret writes: Why is it that when some tragedy strikes and help is urgently required we agoraphobes can all dig into our inner reserves, lift ourselves from the deepest depression and accomplish feats we previously considered an impossibility? At other times we are too self-centered, wallowing in self-pity, maybe feeling a little resentful at being obliged to do mundane boring jobs, jealous of what others achieve, or lazy and lacking the will to apply the effort to overcome our agoraphobia? Maybe our disability is a means of getting us 'off the hook' and thus avoiding the tasks we find distasteful, shopping in the cold, pushing our way through crowds, attending boring functions, waiting on our family and friends? I have been doing quite a bit of introspection lately. Two years ago, although I had been agoraphobic for many years, I was a full time schoolteacher, could travel anywhere by car, and seldom thought of the things I could not do because I was too busy. Then came retirement. I had a beautiful vision of the future. All the time in the world to indulge my whims and fancies — crafts, painting, reading etc. I would do my relaxation exercises every day to enable me to do all the things I had been unable to do — walking to that little shop around the corner, visit the supermarket, visit the hairdresser, attend church etc. I would overcome my agoraphobia.

But what has been the reality? I have done nothing except retreat further and further into the safety of my own home. I don't even walk beyond my own garden gate, and why? I feel dizzy, my legs are wobbly, I might faint, I have palpitations — you know them all. I have read all the books on the subject, listened to endless tapes — they are all really marvellous. I can advise everyone else what they must do to overcome their disability. I could even take the place of the psychologist, but what good is it when I don't pay a bit of notice to it myself? I am an expert at avoidance technique and almost convince myself that my excuses are reasonable and logical. A programme on T.V., however, has brought me back to reality. It showed the hours of gruelling training and determination endured daily by athletes preparing for the Olympics. They go through the pain barrier eight hours a day, six days a week for four years, for what? A medal! If we made one quarter of that sacrifice what would we gain? A far better prize — our freedom. So it's all up to us. I've just begun my training. How about you?

Margaret writes: Looking back over the past year I have achieved a great deal of progress. In January my husband bought me a greenhouse and this has been a marvellous way of being outside whilst still being 'inside'. The joy of growing cucumbers, tomatoes, peppers etc. gave me great pleasure. My interest has now extended to the vegetable garden and at present I am winter digging. This gets me outside. We also bought a small caravan and have got away for two holidays. I was very anxious when we set off for the first time but found my agoraphobia took a holiday also. I was able to go shopping, visit the cinema, in fact I did everything normal whilst away. I manage to walk out alone now, but only at night. I shall keep on trying . . . achieving more each year as I am determined to succeed.

THE DENTIST

Do you dread going to the dentist? This can be even more traumatic if you are also agoraphobic. Only go to the dentist if you want to! All adults are free agents and there is no compulsion for you to go if you would prefer not to. This fact is important because wanting to do something makes it easier to tackle, however unpleasant it might be.

If you are happy to have toothache, to have rotten black teeth or no teeth, bad breath and indigestion, then it is entirely your business — no one else's. If you decide you prefer these things then let no one try to dissuade you. You have the right to choose.

Being undecided is painful and extremely tiring. The expression 'in agony of doubt' is absolutely true. If you are uncertain, allow yourself 48 hours from now, not a minute longer, to decide whether or not to go to the dentist. You can always reconsider your decision at a later date; it does not have to be binding for ever, only just for the present and immediate future. Remember: go to the dentist if you want to, not for any other reason.

Now let us imagine that 48 hours have elapsed . . .

1) You have decided you do not want to go to the dentist and are quite willing to put up with the disadvantages. Right! That is your decision and I respect it. Put all opposite thoughts aside because you have made your decision and are going to stick to it. There is no need to waver and worry any more about whether or not you are going. This is what *you* prefer and *you* want to do. Stop dithering and save yourself anxiety and nervous energy. The decision is made. Do not read any further.

2) On the other hand you may have decided you would prefer to have a healthy, pain-free mouth. Even though you may not enjoy the visit to the dentist you actually *want* to go. Fine, if you want to have your teeth seen to or the pain relieved then you want it over and done with as soon as possible. Make the appointment NOW! If that is impossible, then at the very earliest moment you can. Perhaps you will be lucky and the dentist can see you within a week, so start immediately by saying to yourself 'In a week it will all be over and I will be laughing.' Keep reminding yourself of this.

If you have learnt to relax you can use the various techniques to keep yourself calm during this waiting period and to reduce your general level of anxiety. You can also practise spells of full, deep relaxation and during them rehearse your visit to the dentist step by step. This may sound ridiculous but it is extremely effective. Relax completely then imagine yourself leaving home in good time, travelling there, going into the waiting room, being called into surgery, settling yourself in the chair, talking to the dentist, letting him examine your teeth, perhaps give you an injection, do some drilling, fill the tooth, complete the job and then see yourself getting up from the chair — all done and proud! If you find any part of this upsets you, stop the imagined rehearsal for that session. Start afresh next time you are able to relax. As your appointment draws near continue telling yourself, 'In six days it will be over', 'In five days it will be over' etc. Remind yourself frequently, 'In a week I will be wondering what all the worry was about.'

The day of your appointment arrives. When your name is called start by making the dentist feel at ease and happy. Say 'Good day' and smile! Many people greet their dentist with a scowl and a shudder. Try to imagine how you would feel if that constantly happened to you! Once in the chair make yourself comfortable, let your back and head sink heavily into the cushions, release any tension in your neck, support your elbows on the arms of the chair, let your hands lie palms uppermost — you are less likely to clench them that way — let your knees and feet flop outwards. Relax your whole face with a sigh and when the dentist is ready to begin open your mouth loosely.

There is so much for you to take charge of in that dentist's chair that the time passes faster than you expect, and remember — a relaxed body feels pain far less than does one that is tensed up. Very soon the job will be done and you will have the immense satisfaction of walking out and seeing other people still waiting! This time next week you will be wondering whatever you were worrying about!

It really is worth wanting to go to the dentist — I hope you do!

As with all difficult future situations the anticipation is agonising, so why waste your energy on worry?

We thank Pat for telling us of her experience on visiting the dentist: I absolutely loathed the dentist and from age 6 to 26 didn't go at all. In the last four years I have gone twice to have a tooth out under a brief anaesthetic, which is the answer if you're terrified of extractions. However, two years ago I needed 10 fillings — it may as well have been a trip to the moon! I decided to have the fillings done under a special prolonged anaesthetic (I emphasise *not* the normal anaesthetic) and it cost me an additional £20.00. Believe me, paying over the cash was the nicest part of that experience. For ten days after the treatment I could not sit unsupported in a chair or visit the loo unaided or even eat anything solid. It turned out that one in so many tens of thousands of people have an adverse muscular reaction to the drug that was used — and yours truly drew the short straw!

After that nightmare I was convinced the dentist's chair was akin to some terrible torture of the Spanish Inquisition and I wouldn't entertain the idea of going there even to keep someone else company. Two years went by during which time I suffered agony because of a filling that fell out shortly after it was done. Then a fortnight ago after months of daily headaches due to the pain, I decided I had to go and this time it was to be a dreaded injection or nothing. From the moment I made the appointment I prepared myself slowly and told everyone I knew that I was going to go ahead and do it, so that I would not have to confess to any chickening out. The day before my visit I planned everything I would do, travelling to the surgery, waiting for my name to be called, sitting in the chair relaxing as much as possible during the treatment etc. The day came and I had the injection and the tooth was filled again. I was overjoyed at not having to lose the tooth and I can truly and honestly say that the visit was one of the nicest, easiest experiences I have had. I didn't feel the injection, the dentist explained exactly what he was going to do during each stage, and there was no pain at all. It is amazing how quickly the time went. My fear of visiting the dentist was well and truly conquered and as I was leaving I asked the receptionist to send me a reminder when I would need my six monthly check up!

One other thing: if you go to a dentist for a check up and you are a nervous type, tell the man — he's not a psychic. If his manner is brusque and unsympathetic, I know it's a drag, but leave and try another dentist and another until you find the one who is prepared to help. If we all did this the the very few unpleasant characters would have to change their ways. And let's face it, we agoraphobes are told often enough to change *our* ways!

Mr Francis says: I hope this letter will help others understand and to be able to come face to face with the problem of agoraphobia. Although it has been just a couple of months since I explained to my doctor about my panic attacks, he visited me last week to find I was in a very weak and anxious state. We talked for quite some time and my doctor suggested instead of looking for things to panic about just to await a panic to come on and to *time* it, to see how long these attacks really lasted. I did this and found the attacks lasted only a few minutes at first. Now after a week of going out with my wife and continuing his advice I find they last only a few seconds. I set myself a task every day whether it is a short stand outside my house or a short walk or even to go to the local shop. I find I

105

can do it if I really try. A month ago I could not have done any of these things, now I feel the sky is the limit . . . but am taking it day by day.

A correspondent of mine who wishes to remain anonymous contributes the following thought:

You can if you think you can: It sounds easy doesn't it, but it isn't in the beginning. No, not easy, but worth every second of those tiring, exhausting, despairing first steps outside the front door. I am talking, of course, to those who think they cannot go out alone. I used to be one of you and before you say, as I used to, 'Oh, but you couldn't have been as bad as I am,' let me assure you I was ruled by agoraphobia for most of 19 years. Even to go into the garden to put out the washing was an ordeal . . . sometimes even inside the house I would go upstairs and would be so overcome with symptoms that I would have to come downstairs again on my bottom. Even short car journeys with my husband were a nightmare. I always tried to get my shopping with him at the little local parade but I would return home exhausted and ever despairing. Mild tranquillisers helped keep me from going over the brink of whatever it is we all think is going to happen (but never does). Well, I hope I've convinced you that I was suffering as badly as some of you are now. I hope my letter will help others who are not so bad but would like to recover completely.

I read the self-help books and listened to tapes on helping oneself and as regards outside treatment. I had a course of relaxation at a hospital but was given up as hopeless. Then I was offered desensitisation carried out by another doctor. It meant a car journey of about 15 miles to London but with hope and the help of tranquillisers I managed 6 visits. Sometimes I could not make it, but I did get to go out for the first time on my own (in the dark) just down the road. Then the doctor left the hospital to take up another appointment elsewhere and 60 guinea pigs were left high and dry! But I had made a start. That was in 1970.

I realise now that reading the books and listening to the tapes were really making a good foundation on which to build a slow but steady recovery. How could I hope to get better quickly when it took years of stress, while working and looking after a family, to bring on that first terrible panic whilst out shopping, which was to become part of my life for all those years.

I became interested in deep-breathing (still practised) relaxation before going to sleep each night. By 1974 I was working for my doctor as his receptionist was wanting someone to fill in while she had a holiday. With doubt on my part (and the doctor's I might add) I did a week with her to learn the job and have done this work on and off ever since. I have also worked in a department store as a knitting machine demonstrator. I can honestly say I have never had a panic attack while working. Occasionally I can still get a taste of the old feeling but I go quietly on, knowing it will pass.

If you can make one small effort, however small, and walk *slowly*, breathe deeply — however tired it makes you feel when you get back — you will not be able to give up completely again. It is still a very exciting world outside. Tell yourself you are as important as anyone (some of us feel so guilty and useless when we are ill don't we). Forget all negative thoughts and look for that inner core of self-assurance because it *is* there. The tiredness you feel after your early efforts will gradually become less and less as you lose the tension that is made by your own thinking.

I hope I have given you encouragement to have a go. It really will work, I promise.

After experiencing agoraphobia for 30 years a woman correspondent says triumphantly:

Getting better now: I'd like to pass on these ideas, all of which helped me. A healthy mind in a healthy body: keep physically fit. Use everyone and everything within your orbit. If you can get to the shops, go into every one. Stop the clock or put it in another room — make your own time. Listen to quizzes, talks etc., knit, sew or crochet, tat or paint, learn a language, type, write stories and articles, do competitions (you may even win — we are supposed to be highly intelligent with imaginative minds), join evening classes even if you don't always attend, keep a pet. Never give in, never give up. Think of others worse off. Pray for the blind, paraplegics etc. Pray for yourself. Look outwards. Deep controlled breathing can be enjoyed whilst singing hymns. Get involved.

Finally, let us look at another case history which offers hope.

I was reluctant to go to the doctor so bottled all my agoraphobia up and battled on alone for about twelve months until I was virtually housebound. Then I found the courage to go to my doctor and gradually with his help and by going out a little further each day I have begun the long haul back. I joined the local keep fit class, sang with the choral society and the church choir. I found the more diversions I took the more helpful they became. I found as the years went by I even made myself take holidays, mainly for the family's sake.

My mistake was that I had kept everything to myself for so long. My own parents did not know until it became absolutely necessary for me to explain why I could not visit them (they live 120 miles away), and even now this is sometimes an effort for me. Then after the years of taking the boys to school and coping, which all agoraphobes have to try to live with, I found I was pregnant once again. My daughter was born in 1974 and naturally I was anxious in case depression should set in after her birth. I was so delighted that the baby was perfect that once the early weeks were over I was able proudly to show off my new baby. Not a sign of depression this time as I was elated over my little girl. When she was two years old we moved house and I found it harder to make the effort to do things but I struggled on. I won't pretend it has been easy but with God's help I now feel I have climbed the mountain and can now see the view . . . and this attracts me . . . so my message to other sufferers would be: —

1) Confide in your doctor and follow his instructions implicitly.

2) Do not keep it to yourself, though choose whom you tell with care. People are much kinder than you think.

3) Tell God about it, even if it seems embarrassing at first. Develop your own faith and trust.

4) Try your hardest to develop your interests.

5) Don't be ashamed of your handicap — there are many like us.

6) Go out of your way to help others, whatever their problem. You know what it is like to find an understanding ear.

7 · HOLIDAYS

Are you going on holiday this year? Well now, that's a humdinger of a question, isn't it? You probably will throw up your hands in horror and exclaim, 'Oh, I couldn't, not with my agoraphobia!' It is such a tragedy that so many families, and even single people, miss taking a break away from their surroundings due to an agoraphobic relative who refuses to leave the 'safety' of the home but who will not stay behind alone. Everyone else is put in the position of feeling guilty if they decide to go away regardless, or feels resentful if they have yet again to sacrifice all thoughts of a holiday. Constant refusals on the part of agoraphobes stretch the love between themselves and their families, however caring they may be, to a limit almost beyond endurance as each year goes by.

The real problem of holidays is the trepidation with which they are anticipated. All the 'dreadful things' that might happen in a strange place! Too many 'what if's' fill the mind and body with unnecessary tension.

In contrast, it amazes those who take the plunge, packing all their fears with them, that nothing does happen other than the most pleasant surprise of being able to do many things and face situations without much difficulty; in fact, becoming one's old self again. A holiday often proves the possibility of being able to recover and is the starting point for those resolving never to let themselves become entirely housebound again.

Postcard received by psychiatrist from patient: 'On holiday, having such a lovely time. Why?'

Pauline's holiday afloat: It had been seven years since we had had a holiday. Being a typical agoraphobe of some ten years' standing, the very thought made me shudder and since the births of our two small daughters I had produced every excuse under the sun to avoid going away from home. The girls aged nine and seven started a couple of years ago to ask me why we never went away when all their friends did and my husband looked so weary and fed up that last year I agreed to try and make a special effort. It was my husband's idea, of course, that we should take them to the water. I knew he had cherished a dream for some years that we should take a cabin cruiser and go on the Norfolk Broads, but again the girls had been my excuse. I didn't fancy the Broads really; Norfolk seemed too far away. 'Let's go on our own river,' he suggested after Christmas last year. We live near Reading which is very near the River Thames. We got lots of brochures and found out there were very luxurious cruisers to be rented by the week and that on the Thames we could travel in each direction over a total distance of about ninety miles. The boatyard where we picked up our cruiser was only a short distance away, though that didn't stop me feeling thoroughly miserable and 'aggie-ish' and as we stepped on board I was wishing we had stayed at home. To my surprise the feeling didn't last long. The girls were thrilled with the boat which had all 'mod cons' on board, even a T.V. I felt at home and settled down at once. In fact I felt free as air. Much to my amazement I shopped quite happily in a strange town and the various little villages along the way — knowing my little 'home' was nearby.

We sunbathed on the boat and the girls fished industriously. I really can recommend this type of holiday for agoraphobia sufferers — it certainly seems to suit my type of personality.

I think we agoraphobes must have been snails in an earlier life and now miss having our safe shells to retreat into!

Fear closes the eyes of the mind.

Ethel writes: I am in the position that walking in my own area is very difficult. However, on holiday in the U.K. with husband and car I feel far more relaxed and able to do more. I realise that I am fortunate to be able to go on holiday and I realise that constant repetition and panic in the same areas makes it difficult at home. I am hoping to strike out a bit more and possibly go on a cruise this year. If I do panic I might as well be somewhere glamorous and exciting when doing it!

Good luck to everyone who achieves their objectives, whether to town centres or far away places. We must all move in the best direction so that we can overcome our illness. I have had a few 'downs' this year including an inhibiting back injury and the serious illness of my mother when I nursed her for three months and visited every day when she was in hospital. I felt as if I was living in the ante-room to hell. However, she has made a marvellous recovery, so it was well worth the effort, and I look to the future with hope.

Life is all ups and downs but if I can get aboard that ship I will. I shall have to get to the docks first. If we take the car I should be O.K. but it would be a triumph to get there on the train. Trains at least have corridors and one can get up and move about. My greatest problem is walking out by myself!

Muriel says: I am a lot better (I even got to Holland alone, flying too) but I will not consider myself cured until I can manage coaches easily. Can it be that my coach sick excuse for years is *really* just coach sickness? I can manage trains and now planes but buses churn me up. Going alone is still a trial but I have no relatives, husband or even cousins, and friends are always booked up with their own families and don't need an odd one added on.

Brenda writes: I felt I had to write of my achievements. I have been on holiday for the first time in seven years — not very far away, but I stayed for a whole week without any panics. I was, of course, apprehensive before I went — I'd have given anything to cancel it — but once there I was fine, and I really enjoyed it.

My second achievement is that I have been on a bus by myself (the first time for five years). I went to the village with a friend who was visiting her mother. After she left me I went into the bank, a record shop and then round the market alone! I made the journey home. I want to continue this travelling so that one day I shall make it alone — both ways.

111

Mary tells us: I am writing to say I have just had a wonderful holiday in Canada! It is a place I never thought I would ever go, but our son is out there at University so it was the chance of a lifetime. We did a tour of the Rockies by coach, and I've been on two long plane journeys, on a cable car, over two suspension bridges, on a snowmobile and stayed in an hotel with 42 floors and a revolving restaurant. I am sure it was the benefit of the acupuncture treatment I had before leaving: this did not make any startling change to my agoraphobia, but it made me feel a lot fitter. I have had agoraphobia for about 40 years but felt if I didn't do something really exciting and different I would be too old and life would be slipping by. I had the feeling that should anything happen, someone would take care of things and it wouldn't matter. As it turned out everything was so successful that I am already thinking of my next 'adventure'.

Marg writes: A few weeks ago I was fortunate enough to spend a week at Lee Bay in Devon with my sister and her family. The little bay was so near the hotel that one morning I took my nieces and nephews there for half an hour before breakfast. The hotel was invaded by a T.V. production team making a new series. This was quite interesting as we met quite a few of the actors and the children enjoyed seeing the characters in their costumes.

How lucky I am to be able to get away like this occasionally.

Evelyn tells us: Recently I was chosen to represent working class writers on a working tour of the United States. As you can imagine I was in a most anxious state before we went, hardly eating or sleeping. I had never been in a plane before, nor further than Scotland. I had suffered agoraphobia for many years, three of them housebound. It had only been through my writing I was able slowly to lead a pretty normal life and I work for a writer's group in the city. Reactions to me being chosen ranged from, 'But you can't go — you're agoraphobic' (this from my sister) to 'You lucky so and so' (this from my fellow writer who did not know of my inner struggle). My feelings were mixed. I was petrified, yet it was a chance of a lifetime.

The beginning of May I started off with six other writers from various parts of England. We did not know each other. On the plane we were separated and as soon as we arrived we were rushed off to a reading in New York, unwashed, tired, hungry and thirsty. We had never performed before our first night in America: it was totally unrehearsed. It was one of many performances. I was billetted with a woman who suffered a flare-up

112

of an old back injury, and the responsibility of caring for her certainly helped me forget my own racing pulse. I did have a few panic states but the valuable advice of not 'fighting' the state but to ride over it helped me tremendously at those times. I remembered I was not going to faint or be sick or disgrace myself at all. The rest of the party did not know I had agoraphobia. To them I was highly strung, and a bit 'zany'. We did manage between work to visit Niagara Falls from the Canadian side and I went up the highest building in the world, Sears Tower in Chicago . . . and I'm terrified of lifts and heights. It was great. Along the tours our very good drivers became lost. Again knowing one of our party was in great pain helped me overcome my own panic.

A lot of the tour went wrong, as tours often will; often we slept on couches or on the floor and it was 'different' and exciting. We spent our last 25 hours in America at the John F. Kennedy Airport having run out of money. Even though I would go all over again I did find it had overtaxed my nervous system. I was put off work with nervous exhaustion on my return and still feel the effects and the strain. The trip had been a challenge I met and overcame at the cost of shattered nerves for a while. However, I feel if I could tackle America then I shall, with help, tackle agoraphobia!

Today well-lived makes every yesterday a dream of happiness and every tomorrow a vision of hope.

8 · TREATMENT AND RELAXATION

You have probably been wondering all this time whether treatment other than self-help can be found. In fact, some of you may already have been involved with one or more of the following techniques and found them helpful. If you are reading this, however, you will also have realised that, even when treatment is ended, you are still on your own and will have to cope with whatever situations arise — treatment cannot go on forever, there are just not enough therapists to go round! Some people find themselves becoming dependent on their therapists during treatment and are thus bereft for a while after the sessions are finished. However, if a complete recovery has been made and the patient has regained his or her strong confident personality, then all will be well.

HYPNOTHERAPY

Hypnosis is frequently used to help people who wish to lose weight, or stop smoking, stammering etc., but it can also be used to create confidence through suggestion. It must be stressed most strongly that only medically-trained hypnotherapists should be consulted and on *no* account should you put yourself in the hands of someone who has not been recommended by your doctor or a recognised body of medical or dental hypnotists.

Many people are nervous of hypnotists, fearing that they may be put into a 'trance' (as seen on the stage) but at no time is consciousness ever lost and the subject is aware during the whole session of what is going on and what is being said. Hypnosis just induces a state of deep relaxation, making the mind open to suggestions made by the hypnotherapist who may get you to talk about any hidden anxieties of which you were unable to speak openly before. He or she may then suggest ways in which you can resolve your problems by being more confident in your decisions. These sessions do not usually last long and you will normally feel very relaxed afterwards. Obviously a course of several sessions has to be taken before any real progress can be established.

BEHAVIOUR THERAPY

The principle behind this therapy is the belief that you need to be taught to unlearn some of the bad habits which you have fallen into, such as avoiding certain places, disliking certain situations, becoming obsessive about a particular thing. The techniques used do have a modicum of success if there is only one phobia or obsession to be dealt with. The patient is first taught to relax and then is taken, or shown by means of pictures, the situation he or she fears, or shown the object about which there is an obsession. This kind of treatment also takes many sessions before the patient conquers the fear and can deal happily with the problem without further help.

FLOODING

This is a rather drastic method of attempting to conquer a fear or obsession and would only be adopted after lengthy consultation with the patient to determine whether or not he or she can cope with the treatment. As the name suggests, it entails the patient being 'thrown in at the deep end' as it were, and being confronted with the dreaded object or situation, with no means of escape, until he or she becomes used to the object and anxiety levels drop.

MODELLING

Again the patient is taught to relax, but is afterwards expected to copy the therapist, who goes through the motions of dealing with the patient's particular fear problem as if it were his own. This type of treatment works quite well over a period of time for phobias concerning, for example, animal fur, feathers, snakes. Seeing the therapist stroking and handling the dreaded object should, in theory, help the patient to do likewise. Treatment may well begin with looking at pictures of the object, seeing it through a window, or having it in the same room but in a container (e.g. a cat in a cage), until the anxiety level has dropped to the point where the patients can themselves touch, handle or stroke the object of their phobia.

The following article has been condensed from 'BEHAVIOURISM . . . A framework for common sense therapy'

Walking is healthy, yet few of us take enough exercise. If a doctor advises an obese (fat) patient to take more exercise the chances are that he won't . . . yet persuade his wife to give him a puppy for his birthday and he will probably walk the soles off his shoes for the sake of his dog. Similarly, many housewives lead lives of bitter loneliness only yards away from other women who are longing for their company. It is no good advising them to knock on their neighbours' doors; they just cannot or will not. Yet, provide them with a communal room with washing machine and they will meet and gradually develop friendships. In other words common sense is not enough. The man knows he should walk, the woman knows she should mix with others but they cannot or will not do it unless they are provided with a framework.

At first the method used was de-sensitisation, a very gradual approach to the feared object in fantasy or in fact, with simultaneous relaxation

Recent studies have shown that equal success can be achieved by 'flooding' (implosion) in which the person remains in contact with the feared object for a long time until his fear is exhausted and he can then learn to deal with it without phobia . . . Now all this is common sense. Anyone who has been swimming knows that there are two ways to enter icy water — down the steps gradually or diving in from the deep end. However, in the case of phobias the knowledge is not enough, any more than it is enough for the man to know he must take exercise. So it is not usually effective to sit in the consulting room and tell the agoraphobic patient that he or she might go a little further each day until they have regained their confidence, or that they must go and spend hours in a supermarket until their anxiety is replaced by boredom. The person will not do it.

In the meantime the person must learn to help themselves to get 'desensitised' to situations they do not like. This must be done gradually and although it does take time and perseverance, the reward is great.

HOSPITALISATION

Going into hospital is always available as a last resort for those people who will benefit from being away from their usual surroundings for a short time. These days, so I am told, there are psychiatric wards which almost resemble small hotels, with comfortable surroundings, outings arranged during the day and plenty of 'TLC' from the staff. (TLC, in case you do not know, is 'Tender Loving Care' — something we all need.) On the other side of the coin, however, a stay of this kind sometimes backfires, particularly with women, as they invariably feel much worse when they have to return home. Indeed, home may well have been the reason for their having to go away in the first place!

Having considered just some of the ways in which anxiety can be dealt with, we can see that relaxation is part and parcel of every one, therefore it should be stressed yet again that a new attitude towards life in general, and phobic situations in particular, must be learned before progress of any kind can have a lasting effect. It all comes down to desensitising those over-aroused nerves and feelings before living can again become bearable.

117

RELAXATION

If asked what they consider to be the most important secret of good health, some people would say a good digestion, others a strong heart, but the right answer in every case would be simply the ability to relax. By relaxation, I don't mean a free-and-easy, could-not-care-less attitude to life — this may help you to steer clear of some troubles but the chances are that you will end up with others brought on by laziness. True relaxation is the ability to switch off and forget about your worries and tensions. You would be surprised at the damage, both mental and physical, which results if you cannot do this. Problems with digestion, tension headaches, sleeplessness, chronic acidity, nervous tics, dermatitis and even chain-smoking are generally all due to an inability to relax. Is it any wonder that one out of every five prescriptions is for tranquillisers?

The first step towards achieving a relaxed state of mind and body is to acknowledge the fact that you haven't got it! Phrases like 'I like rushing about' and 'I cannot sit still and do nothing' may reflect an inability to switch off, which arises from inner tension. Equally, an 'always-with-you' feeling of lethargy may also be a sign of tension, as indeed may an excessive tiredness after comparatively small tasks.

Learn to recognise the signs of tension in the early stages. Is your jaw sore because you unconsciously clench it too tightly? Do all your knuckles show white when you grip something? Are you breathing too shallowly and too fast? There are many physical warning signs like this. Be determined to teach yourself the following very simple exercises and do them for about 10 to 15 minutes *every* day without fail, allowing your mind to take control of your body all the time. You will reap the benefits and be aware of a feeling of well-being. Remember that your body is a complex and wonderful creation but it has its limitations; if it has been worked too hard, it will need more time to heal.

Eventually, the new tension-free you will have happier relationships within your family and social circles and an ability to relax properly for 10 minutes a day can add 10 years to your life.

118

EXERCISES

Let us start with the morning, when you awake. Take a few moments before you rise, to s-t-r-e-t-c-h your body along its whole length while lying on your bed. Tense all your muscles, feel the tension and then loosen them. You will soon learn how this feels and it will show you just how tightly you have been holding your body during anxious days. Rise slowly, then do your breathing exercise (see p. 89) before an open window if possible. Just three deep breaths will suffice until you get used to the exercise. Afterwards you will feel able to wash and dress to face the morning.

Concentrate now on the 'time-out' which you promised yourself *every* day. Sit in a comfortable chair, bring all your muscles to a state of tension all over, then loosen. Repeat this twice. Now, starting with your head, place your fingers just behind your ears and move the skin of your scalp gently and slowly, including your forehead; this helps those tension headaches. Next pay attention to your neck, press your head back slightly and rotate it slowly, first one way then the other, and feel how the tension moves.

Shrug your shoulders as high as you can towards ear-level, then let them fall. Do this two or three times to get rid of those aches and pains which plague those tensed muscles.

Now your face. Have you loosened your jaw muscles? Do *not* try doing these little exercises with such determination that your teeth are clenched with effort. Drop your jaw a little, then bite your teeth together. Can you feel the difference?

Drop your arms over the side of your chair loosely, then clench and unclench your fists a couple of times to relax your fingers.

Send messages to your chest and stomach. Breathe gently and slowly, but not exaggeratedly so, whilst pulling in your stomach muscles and then relaxing them. Now think about your back. Lift it away from the chair in an arch, feel the tension, then relax.

Now for your legs. Tense your thigh muscles then let go. Point your toes upwards and tense your calf muscles, let go. Push your feet hard on the floor, let go. Give yourself a few minutes in this completely relaxed state before recommencing your chores or even going out. You will feel better for it.

119

Although total relaxation may seem hard to achieve, and no one can say that relaxation alone will work miracles, at least you can teach yourself to relax certain parts of your body regardless of where you are, thus making a situation easier to deal with. Obviously you cannot carry a chair around with you wherever you go, but who knows — apart from you — that you are relaxing those tense shoulder muscles whilst waiting for a bus, queuing in a supermarket, gaining composure in a crowd of people or preventing that 'jelly-leg' feeling whilst standing to talk to somebody? Any part of your body can be relaxed in this way at any time, provided you have taught yourself some of these simple little tricks in the privacy of your own home. When you become proficient, you will surprise yourself at how easily you slip into the habit, wherever your are.

Mr P. Pellow, a psychotherapist, passes on this idea which he says is successful for some.

This technique called 'anchoring' is very useful. Sit back and relax, go back deep into yourself and recall some moment of the past when everything went just right for you, and you were in total control confident, happy. With your eyes closed, bring this as strongly into mind as you can, using vision, hearing sounds or words of that time. Taste any tastes, smell any smells associated with the memory — feel it in your body and feel it in your emotions. When it is at its strongest, put your right hand down and squeeze your right knee gently but firmly. Repeat several time a day over two or three weeks and you will eventually find that by simply squeezing your right knee, or wherever you choose, the good feelings will flow through you. This is similar to feeling hungry when the dinner gong sounds.

PREPARING FOR BED

Now you have come to the end of the day and are preparing for a good night's rest and a summing up of all those relaxing thoughts. Do not take problems to bed with you — they will seem different tomorrow. Equally never go to bed with a quarrel on your mind resolve it before the lights go out. Sprinkle a generous handful of bath salts into a warm bath (do not shower at night, it is too stimulating), lie back and let the fragrance soothe the nerves. Pat yourself dry (harsh rubbing is stimulating too) and then brush your hair smoothly and gently. All this helps you to feel rested. Go to bed and repeat the little 'before-rising' exercise of tensing all your muscles and then letting go a couple of times, relax your jaw, eyes, arms, all the way down your body to your toes. Breathe deeply and gently and feel that relaxed feeling coming over you. If you have made a warm drink in readiness, perhaps containing honey, which is supposed to be a sedative, sip this and feel languid enough to put out the light and . . . *good night!*

CONCLUSION

Let us now end this book with a summary of the most important points. Very many readers will not, by any means, have suffered from all of the symptoms or difficulties mentioned, but it is to be hoped that they will have gained some insight and optimism regarding any problems presently bothering them. The following lists should be helpful to every sufferer, even in the recovery stage.

Do not . . .

1. . . . keep your problems, difficulties and anxieties to yourself all the time. Please discuss them with your family, friends or neighbours and, above all, your doctor.
2. . . . shut yourself away from all human contact. You can do without material things but you cannot do without people.
3. . . . worry continually about trifles which will probably resolve themselves without your efforts anyway!
4. . . . rush around trying to carry everyone else's problems on your own shoulders; offer help, but you are not superhuman.
5. . . . create a habit of being anxious about any future event. The chances are you will probably enjoy it!
6. . . . say *no* continually to any family member, friend or neighbour etc., who asks you to accompany them somewhere, even to the shops.
7. . . . lie in bed all day, thinking it will kill time; it doesn't — it makes it drag on longer.

Now DO

1. . . . make lists, lots of them. List your problems in order of priority and deal with the smaller ones first. The big ones may resolve themselves by the time you have finished.

2. . . . talk to your family, friends, neighbours or doctor, by all means, but don't bore them to death every day with the same thing.

3. . . . remember that, even with no treatment whatsoever, depression often lifts and passes off, given time.

4. . . . try to keep optimistic at all times, particularly towards your own recovery. It can be done, patiently, a little at a time.

5. . . . remember, if you are alone, *you* are the one who has to boost your own confidence, coddle yourself from time to time, set that meal tray nicely and enjoy it in a relaxed state, keep your looks. All this helps to remind you that you are still a person of worth in your own right.

6. . . . keep a radio going, even quietly, whilst at home alone. There is nothing more lonely than an empty silent house. Television very often offers 'visual' company to some people.

7. . . . talk to yourself sometimes when you are alone. You are not 'going round the bend' and it will help to make your voice seem less strange when you do have a visitor or meet someone outside. After all, the old saying about all muscles is 'If you do not use it, you lose it!'

8. . . . remember, there is a light at the end of every tunnel — however dark the way seems just now.

These are just a few suggestions to consider. On reflection, you should be able to add more of your own, which are suited to your lifestyle, whether you are at home, in an office or perhaps in a place of learning.

Lists or notes are invaluable if, in your anxious state, you tend to forget dates and appointments, etc. They can help to give your confidence a boost if, for example, you are able to answer a question correctly because you took the trouble to 'make a note'.

A final word to those of you who maybe have not ventured out of your house, flat or room for a long time. Have you remembered the first trick you learned when reading the beginning of the book? Teach yourself to *close* that door — with you on the outside — but holding the key in your hand? If not, do *please* try — it becomes easier as each day goes by.

Remember, I have been along that road to hell and back, from the days in the 1960s when I would not even *open* the door, let alone go through it, to the life I lead today. Only too well do I know those strange feelings with which you regard the outside world.

Now let us suppose that you feel able to tackle that little walk, perhaps in the evening — some people prefer starting their first walks during the later hours, feeling that the darkness gives them a sense of anonymity and calmness. So, on with your jacket. Pop this little book in your pocket as a reminder that you are no longer alone, for I am going with you for that walk. *Good luck*!

Our doubts are traitors,
And make us lose the good we oft might win
By fearing to attempt.

Measure for Measure
Shakespeare

USEFUL ADDRESSES

UNITED KINGDOM

Al-Anon Family Groups, 61 Great Dover Street, London SE1 4YF (Help for families of alcoholics)

Alcoholics Anonymous, PO Box 514, 11 Redcliffe Gardens, London SW10 (Advice and help for those suffering from alcoholism)

British Migraine Association, 'Evergreen', Ottermead Lane, Ottershaw, Surrey KT16 0HJ (Help for sufferers through leaflets, newsletters etc.)

Cruse Clubs, Cruse House, 126 Sheen Road, Richmond, Surrey TW9 1UR (Help and encouragement for widows, widowers and children)

Gingerbread, 35 Wellington Street, London W1 (Help for one-parent families)

Health Education Council, 78 New Oxford Street, London WC1A 1AH (Leaflets on a variety of health problems)

Mama, 26A Cumnor Hill, Oxford (Support for women suffering from post-natal depression)

MIND (National Association for Mental Health), 22 Harley Street, London W1N 2ED (General advice and leaflets)

Open Door Association, c/o 447 Pensby Road, Heswall, Wirral, Cheshire L61 9PQ (Send stamped addressed envelope for information sheet on tape cassettes, self-aid schemes etc. for agoraphobics)

Patients Association, 11 Dartmouth Street, London SW1 (Gives help and advice to individuals regarding National Health Service complaints)

U and I Club, 9E Compton Road, London N1 2AP (Advice and help for sufferers of cystitis etc.)

UNITED STATES OF AMERICA

Behaviour Therapy Institute, Beverley Hills, California 90212

Behaviour Therapy Institute, Sausalito, California 94965

Institute for Behaviour Therapy, 354 East 76th Street, New York NY10021 (Private treatment)

White Plains Hospital Phobia Clinic, 41 East Post Road, White Plains, New York (Hospital treatment)

NEW ZEALAND

Association of New Zealand Agoraphobics Inc., PO Box 7053, Palmerston North, New Zealand

AUSTRALIA

State Wide Agoraphobia Group Inc., 14 Mitchell Street, Glengowrie, South Australia 5044

CANADA

Freedom from Fear Foundation, Box 261, Etobicoke, Ontario M9C 4V3

INDEX